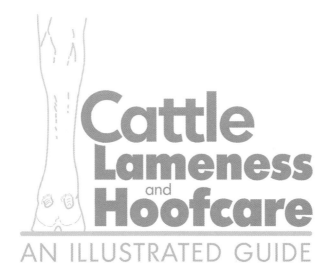

Cattle Lameness and Hoofcare

and

AN ILLUSTRATED GUIDE

Cattle Lameness and Hoofcare

AN ILLUSTRATED GUIDE

Roger Blowey
BSc, BVSc, FRCVS

SECOND EDITION

Old Pond
PUBLISHING LTD

First published 1993, reprinted 1998
Second edition 2008, reprinted 2012

Published by Old Pond Publishing Ltd
Dencora Business Centre
36 White House Road
Ipswich
IP1 5LT
United Kingdom

www.oldpond.com

Distributed in North America by
Diamond Farm Book Publishers
PO Box 537
Alexandria Bay, NY13607, USA

www.diamondfarm.com

A Catalogue record for this book is available from the British Library

ISBN 978-1-905523-28-3

Frontispiece: the stance of a cow affected by laminitis/coriosis.

Photographs by Roger Blowey unless otherwise credited
Cover design and book layout by Liz Whatling
Printed in China for Compass Press

Contents

Foreword to the first edition by Peter Kloosterman

A lot has happened in modern dairy husbandry during the last twenty-five years. Changes in housing, feeding etc. have been enormous and these have had their effect on dairy cows, not least on milk yield. Farmers these days ask a lot more from their cows.

Therefore management on the farm becomes more and more important. The farmer himself can minimise foot disease and foot problems by feeding his cows sensibly, maintaining clean and dry housing, using footbaths, and by sound breeding. One major aspect of management, described in this book, is hoofcare.

I like to emphasise the need for preventive foot trimming. It is a well-known fact that claws overgrow and eventually cause lameness by sole ulcers, white line defects etc. If hoofcare is carried out regularly, ulceration of the sole can be prevented. If the quick becomes bruised, the cow will change its posture and gait in order to relieve pain. This can be recognised by the farmer and is a good reason to trim the feet. Prevention is better than cure.

In the Netherlands it is accepted that cows' feet should be regularly trimmed, twice each year, preferably in spring and in autumn. Even so, laminitis remains a difficult condition requiring a lot of attention. Individual cases are hard to prevent where there is a herd problem. In his book Roger Blowey gives a good picture of foot diseases and how to deal with and prevent them.

I have read the book with pleasure and feel that it can significantly contribute to proper footcare on farms.

Pieter Kloosterman, Teacher in Hoofcare Dairy
Training Centre Friesland (DTC-Friesland),
Oenkerk, The Netherlands

Author's Preface to the Second Edition

At first it was very tempting to simply do a reprint of this book and leave the effort of a second edition for another few years. I then looked at all the new information that had accumulated over the past ten years and thought better of it! The basic anatomy of the foot has clearly not changed since the first edition was printed in 1993, but we have advanced our understanding of the pathogenesis of disorders of the foot, and especially of the changes that occur around the time of calving. This was one of the sections that was updated in the 1998 reprint of the book, and further changes were needed again this time.

Much of the new information presented originates from meetings of The International Ruminant Digit Symposia, held every two years at a different venue worldwide. These have been excellent meetings and I would like to thank the many colleagues who have attended, presented papers and freely discussed the results of their research with me.

I have increased the detail in the book, describing new conditions such as heel ulcers and toe necrosis, and I have expanded the number of pictures. We know that colour pictures are of great benefit, and hence the inclusion of another thirty will surely enhance the quality of the overall book. The text is aimed mainly at farmers, veterinarians and foot trimmers in practice, i.e. those who are at the very forefront of the problem of cattle lameness on a day-to-day basis. If this book helps them with an increased understanding of lameness, or even simply increases their enthusiasm for battling with an ever-present task, then I shall be well pleased.

Roger Blowey
Gloucester
March 2008

Acknowledgements

Almost all the photographs in this book have been taken on farms in the course of my day-to-day general practice and I would like, once again, to acknowledge the patience and understanding of the many Gloucestershire farmers who waited, often at the most inconvenient times, while I went away to get my camera!

Special thanks must go to Jane Upton, for her excellent preparation of the diagrams, and to Catherine Girdler, who so proficiently tackled the typing of the original manuscript. Both have made a major contribution towards this book.

I learned a lot from the Warwick Group in both the Biotin and EU LAMECOW projects, and I would like to thank Laura Green, Jon Amory, Zoe Barker, Jo Wright and Adrian Packington for involving me with this work.

I would like to acknowledge the help of Bob Ward for instructive discussions on the first edition, Pete Ossent, Karl Burgi, David Logue, Susan Kempson, Janet O'Connell and David Pepper for the use of their material, the staff at Old Pond Publishing and Farming Press for their patience and help during the preparation of the Second Edition and the original book, and of course Pieter Kloosterman who has so kindly read the manuscript and written the Foreword. Thanks are due to the *Veterinary Record* and Wolfe Publications who have published some of the photographs previously in *In Practice, A Colour Atlas of Diseases and Disorders of Cattle* and *Self-Assessment Tests in Veterinary Medicine*. Finally, thanks must go to my wife, Norma, for continued tolerance, patience and support.

Dedicated to my Parents

CHAPTER ONE

The Incidence and Costs of Lameness

Lameness, as every farmer knows, is a major cost to the dairy herd. This 'cost' has three main components: the economic losses resulting from reduced production; the labour costs associated with the treatment and husbandry of chronically lame animals, and the welfare costs of suffering to the individual affected cow. Lameness is undoubtedly a major welfare problem. It is also the condition which accounts for the third largest loss of income in the dairy herd, dwarfed only by mastitis and poor fertility. At worst, affected cows have to be culled. This increases overall culling rates and hence replacement costs.

In those cows which can be treated, there is often a dramatic weight loss, milk yield falls and, in protracted cases in early lactation, fertility is affected. In addition, there will be the costs of treatment, whether on-farm labour is used or veterinary attention is sought. If antibiotics are administered milk may have to be discarded.

One UK study, in which the author took part, involving over 1,100 cow years on trial, showed that on average each case of lameness, ranging form a mild digital dermatitis to a more severe sole ulcer, led to a yield reduction of almost 400 litres, and that the start of this reduced yield could be detected for up to four months prior to the lameness being first noticed (49).* This strongly suggests that there are changes occurring in the foot well before lameness becomes apparent.

The same study showed that cows which go lame are generally the higher yielders in the group, and many other papers have shown a similar relationship between higher yields and lameness. A second study by the same group of authors (3) involving 1,824 lame cows, showed a yield decrease of 570 litres for a case of lameness caused by a sole ulcer and 370 litres for a case of white line lameness. Although it was not significant, the study also found that for each case of digital dermatitis treated, yield increased by 1.0 litres.

One of the most dramatic changes seen in lame cows is undoubtedly weight loss. It is surprising how many cows continue to milk, especially in the early stages of lameness, although weight loss can be dramatic. Farmers who have out-of-parlour computer feeders have often commented that reduced concentrate intake is seen some twenty-four hours before lameness is noticed.

In a study (103) of grazing animals, it was shown that lame cows spent longer lying down and less time grazing, and even when they did graze, bite rates were lower. However, a second study showed that although lame cows spent longer lying in cubicles, when they did eat their intake at each meal was greater than in non-lame cows (73). Lame cows lose the ability to defend themselves and get pushed further down the scale of 'social dominance'. They tend to be last to access the food, later entering the milking parlour (which means that they stand for longer at each milking) and more restless in the parlour than non-lame animals.

Not surprisingly, fertility is also affected. A detailed study of 427 cases of lameness in seventeen dairy herds in Somerset (33) showed that affected cows took between 0 and 40 days (an average of fourteen days) longer to get back in calf, depending on the stage of lactation when the cow was first affected, the cause of the lameness and its severity. Some cows did not recover, of course, and hence culling rates were increased. Yields were

---

* Bracketed numbers refer to references, page 124

depressed by between 1 and 20 per cent, depending on the severity of the lameness.

A late-lactation cow with a mild case of foul in the foot or digital dermatitis is easily treated and suffers virtually no adverse effects. A severe, penetrating ulcer with secondary infection of the navicular bursa or pedal joint can lead to the loss of the cow and obviously a substantial loss of income.

The Incidence of Lameness

The incidence of lameness varies between farms, with quoted figures for well-recorded herds varying between 4 and 55 per cent of cows affected each year (91), with an average case incidence of around fifty cases per hundred cows per year. 'One case' is defined as one foot affected once, so if a cow is lame in, for example, both hind feet, then this is two cases of lameness. This wide variation partly arises from the source of the survey material. If veterinary practice records are used, then a lower incidence is obtained (4.7–5.5 per cent) (44, 90). However, taking combined veterinary and farm treatments gives an annual incidence of approximately 25 per cent of cows in the national herd being treated for lameness each year (5, 104). Considerably more cows than this need corrective hoof-trimming, and this incidence has persisted over several years from the late 1980s and early 1990s (61) until well into the 21st century.

One might question why, after so many years of research, the incidence of lameness has not decreased. There is no one single answer, but it is likely to be because many of the factors that predispose to lameness (increased yields, high concentrate feeding, larger herds, changing from straw yards to cubicles/freestalls) have become more of a feature of the dairy industry. In addition, digital dermatitis, first reported in Italy in 1972, then in the UK in 1985, has now become widespread, and accounts for 20 per cent of all lame cows. For example, in one UK study (22) where the overall incidence of recorded lameness was almost seventy cases per hundred cows per year, the incidence of sole ulcers, white line lesions and digital dermatitis were all equal at approximately twelve cases per hundred cows per year, with 'foul' being slightly lower at seven per hundred per year.

In another study (3) involving fifty UK herds monitored for three years, 35 per cent of cows went lame, and the case incidence was 6.8 cases per 100 cows per year for sole ulcers, 5.4 for white line disease, 6.3 for digital dermatitis and 5.6 cases/100/year for 'other' lesions. This confirms that these three disorders are the major causes of lameness in the UK

A survey carried out in the late 1970s (90) showed that leg disorders accounted for only 12 per cent of the total number of cases of lameness recorded and that these were mainly calving injuries. This means that 88 per cent of lameness was associated with the foot. Of these, the majority (86 per cent) were in the hind feet, with the outer claw (85 per cent) being the most likely to be affected. As front feet are much more difficult to restrain and treat, perhaps it is just as well that they are not so commonly involved!

Quantifying the Financial Costs of Lameness

The losses of yield and the effects on fertility and culling were given earlier in this section. In an assessment of the total losses associated with lameness, Esslemont (45) estimated that lameness cost the dairy industry in England and Wales £90 million per year (1990 values) or £31.50 for every cow in your herd! He also estimated that the average cost of lameness in a typically affected cow was £227–£297 for a sole ulcer, £139–£153 for digital disease (white line infection, sole abscess or sole penetration), and £24–£58 for interdigital disease (foul, dermatitis, skin hyperplasia, etc.), the major proportion of these costs arising from the effects of lameness in early lactation on subsequent fertility and culling rates.

These figures do not take into account the

welfare of the cow, or the additional work and frustration caused to the herdsman in the treatment, husbandry and management of such cows. Since that time the profitability of the dairy industry has fallen but it is likely that the cost of lameness has remained the same

Assessing Lameness by Locomotion Scoring

At one stage we thought it was obvious when a cow was lame. She was holding her leg and not taking weight. It is now recognised that lameness can be detected at a much earlier stage than this by watching her as she walks. This is known as 'locomotion scoring', and if the whole herd is locomotion scored it gives an indication of the overall level of foot problems in the herd. Several systems of locomotion scoring have been proposed, but probably the most popular is a modified system originally devised by Sprecher *(92)*.

1. *Sound.* Cow stands and walks with her back level and takes long strides.
2. *Slightly lame.* Stands with level back but walks with arched back and takes shorter strides. Does not favour any obvious limb.
3. *Moderate lameness.* Stands and walks with arched back. Moves with short strides; reduced weight bearing can be detected on affected leg. Head drops when weight is taken on affected leg.

4. *Severe lameness.* Back arched when standing and walking, with obvious reduced weight bearing on affected limb. Cow moves slowly, often making frequent stops, and may show secondary signs of pain such as weight loss, teeth grinding and excess salivation.
5. *Extreme.* Back arched, unable to move. Does not take weight on the affected leg.

This system is often modified to a simple three-point locomotion score, namely:
1. standing and walking with a flat back
2. standing or walking with back arched
3. walking but favouring one limb, i.e. limping.

About this Book

So, what can be done about this expensive disease? The objectives of this book are:

- to give the reader a better understanding of the anatomy of the foot and the importance of its weight-bearing surfaces
- to see what happens during overgrowth and how this results in the foot becoming destabilised.
- to discuss and demonstrate the principles of foot-trimming
- to describe and illustrate the various disorders of the foot that lead to lameness
- to examine some of the more important aspects of lameness prevention.

CHAPTER TWO

Foot Structure, Function and Inflammation *(Laminitis)*

THE STRUCTURE OF THE FOOT

Many technical terms will be used throughout this book. This is in an attempt to increase the precision of the descriptions and is certainly not intended to confuse the reader. By initially explaining and defining the terms and then by using them repeatedly throughout the text, it is hoped that they will become easily understood and part of 'comfortable' language.

The foot consists of two separate digits, the outer or lateral claw and the inner or medial claw. Illus. 2.1 shows a bovine right hind foot, viewed from the bottom and from the side. Note how the lateral claw is slightly larger than the medial. In front feet this is reversed, with the medial claw being larger than the lateral. The outer wall of each claw is known as the abaxial surface and the inner wall, facing the space between the claws, is the axial surface. The space between the claws is known as the interdigital cleft and this separates the two heel bulbs. The front surface of the foot, from the coronary band to the toe, is known as the anterior aspect or anterior wall, and the rear, at the heel, the posterior aspect.

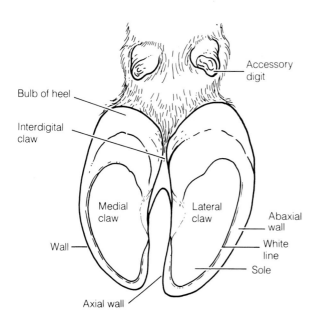

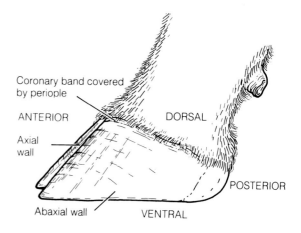

The two claws are highly modified forms of the second and third human fingers (Illus. 2.2). However, whereas our fingernail only covers the front surface of our finger, the cow's hoof forms a complete covering around the digit. The first and fourth fingers are equivalent to the accessory digits, and the thumb has totally disappeared.

2.1   The right hind foot viewed from the bottom *(above)* and from the side *(right above).*

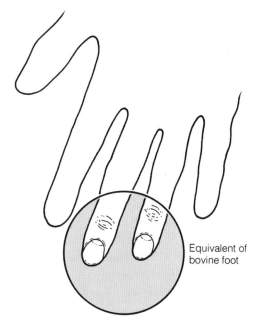

2.2   The human hand compared to the bovine foot.

Equivalent of bovine foot

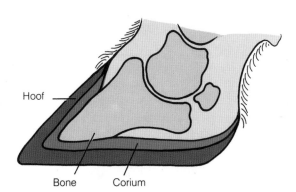

Hoof

Bone   Corium

2.3   The three basic tissues of the foot: hoof, corium and bone.

The claw consists of three basic tissue components (Illus. 2.3). Starting from the outside these are:

- The hoof (the epidermis), which is the hard outer casing of the foot.
- The corium or quick (the dermis) contains nerves and blood vessels carrying nutrients for hoof formation and also acts as a support structure to suspend the pedal bone within the hoof.
- The pedal bone, navicular bone and their associated structures bear the weight from the body and transfer it into the foot.

Some texts refer to an additional layer, the subcutis, which separates the corium (dermis) from the bone, and contains cylindrical fat pads for shock absorption. In this text I have included the subcutis as part of the dermis.

The horn of the hoof is the extensively modified superficial layer of the skin (technically known as the epidermis) which has become expanded and impregnated with a sulphur-containing hardener known as keratin. The corium is equivalent to the dermis or lower part of the skin, and although the corium provides nutrition for the hoof, it is the layer of epidermis lining the corium that secretes and produces the hoof. Technical texts subdivide the hoof and the corium into various layers. These are listed below for reference.

Hoof (epidermis):
- stratum corneum
- stratum granulosum
- stratum spinosum
- stratum germinativum.

Basement membrane (the junction between the epidermis and the corium)

Corium (dermis):
- stratum lamellatum (laminae) or papillarae (papillae)
- stratum vasculosum
- stratum periostale (periosteum).

THE HOOF

The hoof can be subdivided into five component areas:

- the periople
- the wall
- the sole
- the white line
- the heel.

These structures are all shown in Illus. 2.4. This diagram will need to be referred to regularly during the reading of this section.

The Structure of the Foot

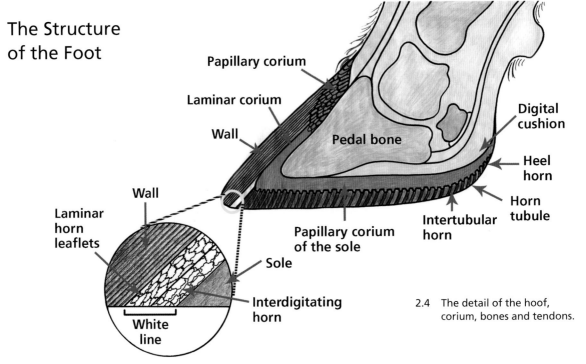

2.4 The detail of the hoof, corium, bones and tendons.

The periople

The periople is the hairless band of soft horn which separates the hoof wall from the skin at the coronary band and is clearly seen in Illus. 2.5. It is continuous from one claw to the other, merging with the bulb of the heel, and acts as a junction between the flexible skin and the rigid wall of the keratinised hoof wall. The periople is responsible for the smooth, waxy coating seen over the front of good quality hooves. Its function is to prevent excess water loss and hence keep the foot supple.

Unfortunately, it deteriorates with age and with hot, dry, sandy conditions underfoot. When perioplic horn is damaged, for example, during very dry weather, the hoof wall may crack, producing a vertical fissure, more commonly known as a sandcrack (see Illus. 5.36).

The wall

The wall of the hoof is equivalent to the human fingernail, except that it wraps itself around the whole structure, rather than just covering the front of the finger. Again like our nail, the wall is formed at the skin–horn junction, and it is effectively extruded by the papillae, small finger-like projections of the corium, sited just below the coronary band. Illus. 2.6 and 2.7 show how the wall is thinner at this point. The papillae are covered by the stratum germinativum, or germinative layer, of the epidermis. This is the basic microscopic layer which is responsible for horn formation.

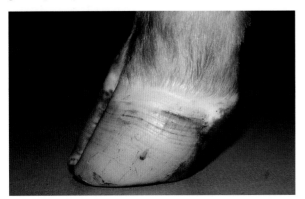

2.5 Lateral view of the claw, showing the periople and steep angle of the anterior hoof wall.

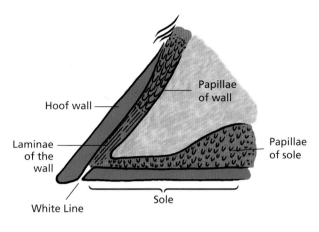

2.6   Section through the foot showing the papillae, laminae and white line.

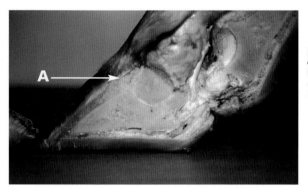

2.7   Transverse section of the foot. Note how the hoof wall is thinner in the region of the papillae, just below the coronary band (A). The thick, glistening white flexor tendon runs down the rear of the navicular bone to attach to the base of the pedal bone.

To increase its strength, the cells of the hoof are arranged in a series of pipes or tubules, the growth of each tubule being effectively an extrusion process from the papilla (Illus. 2.8). Tubules are sometimes said to be equivalent to steel reinforcing bars in concrete.

Horn tubules are glued together by further keratin-containing *intertubular horn* originating from the sides and base of the papillae (Illus. 2.4 and 2.8). In the wall at the toe there are approximately eighty tubules per square mm, although towards the heel, where the horn is softer, the tubule density in the wall is lower. The sole contains only fifteen to twenty tubules per square mm, and is weaker still – as we all know

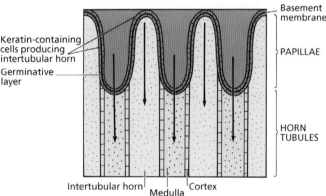

2.8   Detailed structure of the papillae, producing horn tubules and intertubular horn.

Hoof horn consists of horn tubules (from the tips of the papillae) and intertubular horn (from the sides and crypts of the papillae) These cells are filled with a sulphur-containing hardener (the onychogenic substance) which matures in the stratum spinosum to produce keratin, an extremely hard substance. Maturation of keratin involves the oxidation of the sulphur-containing amino acid cysteine to form cystine. The majority of the hoof wall consists of the stratum corneum, the mature, hardened layer. Keratin is also present in hair, in the enamel of teeth and, to a lesser extent, in the superficial layers of our skin.

when trimming feet! Illus. 2.4 depicts the tubules in the sole as being larger than the tubules in the wall. This is not correct: they should be the same diameter, there are just fewer tubules and more intertubular cement

The tubules run longitudinally down the front of the hoof and vertically down through the sole. Intertubular horn is softer than tubular horn, but the number of horn tubules in a hoof is fixed at birth. This means that as a hoof gets larger, it does so by an expansion of intertubular horn and hence a very large, flat foot in a cow is generally softer and weaker than the small, compact hoof of a heifer. This is one reason why the incidence of white line defects doubles with each parity, e.g. for an incidence of two cases per hundred cows per year in first lactation heifers, there are 4 cases/100 in second lactation, 8 cases/100 in the third, and 16 cases /100 in fourth.

Once formed, the wall passes slowly down over the front of the foot, at a rate of approximately 5mm per month. As in the average foot the distance from the coronary band to the wearing surface at the toe is approximately 75–80 mm (and longer for bigger cows), this means that the horn at the toe will not come into wear until sixteen months after it has been produced (80 mm divided by 5 mm per month). Clearly, towards the heel, where the wall is often only half this height, the horn comes into wear sooner.

To achieve weight bearing the hoof wall needs to be firmly attached to the underlying structures which it protects and yet, at the same time, it must pass down over the hoof wall and have a small amount of movement in order to act as a shock absorber during locomotion. These dual functions are achieved by a series of leaves, known as the lamellae, which run down the inside of the hoof wall and interdigitate with the laminae of the corium. This is discussed in more detail in the section on the corium. Illus. 2.9 is a boiled-out specimen of a hoof which shows the lamellae very well. There are some 1,300 laminae in total, arranged like the gills of a fish, and all are present at birth.

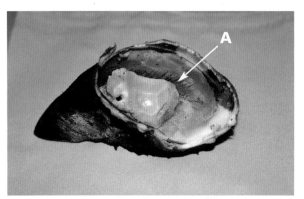

2.9   A boiled-out specimen of the hoof, showing pink laminae running down the inside of the hoof wall (A) and the position of the pedal bone inside the hoof.

The movement of the hoof wall down over the laminae has been compared to one piece of corrugated cardboard (the wall) moving down a second, stationary piece (the corium – Illus. 2.10). The corrugations of the laminae are much deeper than those of the cardboard, of course, giving much greater support and adhesion.

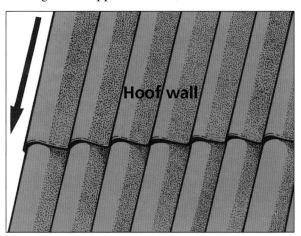

2.10 A diagrammatic representation of the laminae – one sheet of corrugated cardboard sliding over another.

The sole

Earlier we said that the wall of the hoof was equivalent to our fingernail. However, if the cow walked on the skin at the end of her 'finger' she would soon wear it through, so to avoid this she has a second layer of horn effectively growing out from 'finger tip'. This is known as the sole, and it is a structure that is totally separate from the wall, with a different origin.

The horn of the sole is formed from papillae on the sole and hence consists of horn tubules and an intertubular matrix (Illus. 2.11). There are no laminae in the sole and the solear horn grows directly downwards from the corium beneath the pedal bone. Hence when we hear of 'laminitis' affecting the sole, this cannot be technically correct, although the term is, of course, often used. The sole has only fifteen to twenty tubules per square mm (although there is some variation across the sole), and as such the sole does not have the same strength as the wall.

2.11 The structure of the hoof wall, sole and white line.

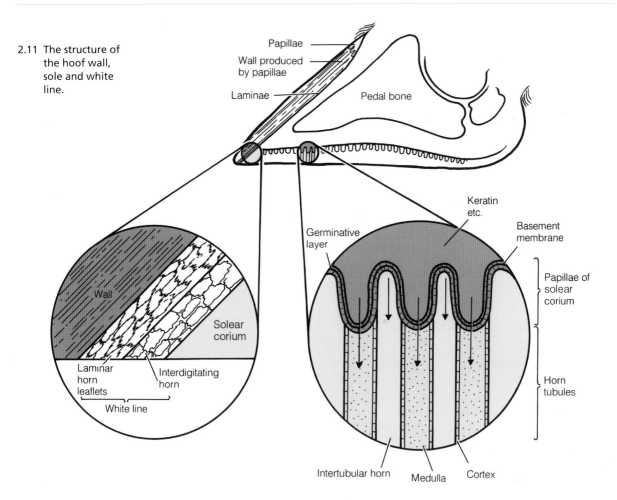

The white line

Although the wall and sole are separate structures, they clearly must be joined together, and the cemented junction between the two structures is known as the white line. The white line can be clearly seen in Illus. 2.12, 2.13, 4.16 and 2.4. It runs from the bulb of the heel to the toe and then back along the first third of the axial wall, and when the wall is no longer a weight-bearing surface, the white line runs up towards the axial space. The position of the white line can be seen on the axial (right) wall of Illus. 2.14 and 2.15 where the laminar corium is less pronounced. There are no horn tubules in the white line. It consists of cells cemented together, and as such, it is a point of weakness and a common site for impaction of debris and entry of infection.

2.12 Transverse section of the hoof. The white of the white line and its junction with the hoof wall are clearly visible.

Why is the white line white? This is probably because movement of the wall over the laminae is achieved by the laminae producing small quantities of horn, sometimes known as the laminar horn leaflet cells (69). Their position is shown

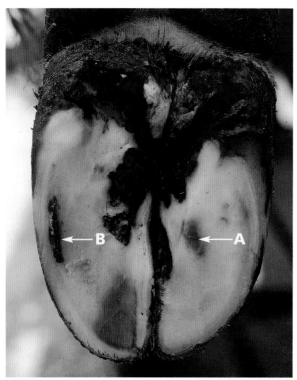

2.13 A sole haemorrhage. Note blood at the sole ulcer site (A) and at the white line (B). The black at the toe is the normal hoof pigment.

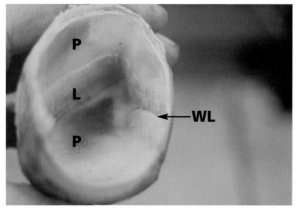

2.14 Internal view of the hoof showing the position of the papillary (P) and laminar (L) corium, and the white line (WL).

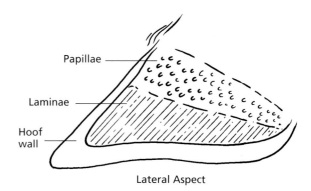

Lateral Aspect

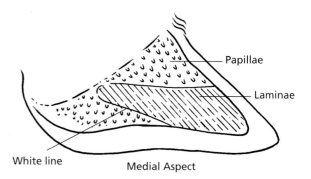

Medial Aspect

2.15 Note how the laminar corium on the abaxial (outer) wall is much wider than on the axial wall. The white line can be seen running up the inside of the hoof on the axial wall (lower diagram).

diagrammatically in Illus. 2.11 and the white line can be clearly seen in Illus. 2.12. The horn leaflets produced by the laminae consist of long, thin cells, running parallel with one another (Illus. 2.16). Where the laminae of the wall end and the papillae of the sole start, there is a small intermediate area which produces 'interdigitating horn', that is horn which connects the wall to the sole. This consists of flat, irregular-shaped cells, again containing keratin (Illus. 2.17). There are no horn tubules in this part of the white line and this, combined with the shape of the interdigitating horn cells, is thought to account for both the inherent weakness of the area and also for its ability to move slightly during weight-bearing, returning to its original shape when at rest (62).

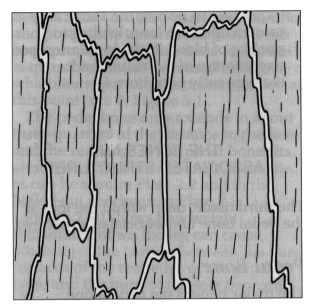

2.16 Well-organised, elongated squame cells from laminar leaflet horn. Keratin fibres are straight and the cell junctions are tight. *(D. Logue and S. Kempson)*

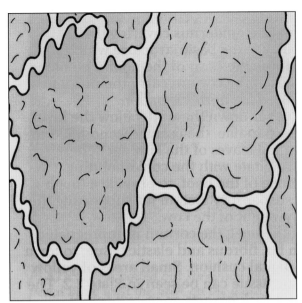

2.17 Rounded squame cells from the interdigitating horn. Keratin is present, but the fibres are not elongated. *(D. Logue and S. Kempson)*

We have already seen how the process of keratinisation (hardening) starts in the inner layer of the hoof, but full maturation of keratin does not occur until it reaches the outer layers (the stratum corneum). The lower levels of the laminae are also non-pigmented. The white line therefore consists of immature laminar horn leaflets joined to the sole by interdigitating horn. This immature horn is non-pigmented and hence the term *white* line. It is also incompletely keratinised, and therefore considerably weaker. The distinct junction of the wall with the horn of the white line is clearly seen in Illus. 2.12 The white line is narrow on the axial (inside) aspect of the claw, but widens on the abaxial (outer) aspect, especially towards the heel. This is one reason why white line defects (impaction and infection) are more common in the abaxial (outer) wall at the sole heel junction (site 1, Illus. 5.1 and zone 3, Illus. 5.5) than elsewhere in the foot.

The heel

The heel, or bulb of the hoof, is a rounded area covered by softer horn, a continuation of the perioplic layer. It is tubular horn, and the tubules 'bend' to run around the curvature of the heel towards the sole. Being flexible, the heel leads to compression of the underlying subcutis layer of the corium during weight-bearing and returns to normal when pressure is removed. These continual changes in shape put considerable pressure on the adjacent, more rigid hoof wall, however. This has been suggested as a further reason why white line disease (impaction and infection) is more common in the abaxial (outer) wall at the sole-heel junction (site 1, Illus. 5.1) than elsewhere in the foot *(82)*.

THE CORIUM

The second tissue within the claw is the corium or quick. Whereas the hoof was the modified epidermis, or outer layer of the skin, the corium is the modified dermis. The corium is the support tissue of the foot. It contains nerves and blood vessels for both the hoof and pedal bone, and it carries the nutrients required for horn formation and for feeding the periosteum which surrounds the pedal bone. Whereas the horn of the hoof is dead, the corium is very much alive. When damaged it will bleed and cause pain.

The corium can be subdivided into:

- Papillary corium - extrudes the horn.
- Laminar corium – supports the wall as it passes down over the foot and provides a tight suspensory attachment for the pedal bone to the front wall of the hoof.
- Digital cushion – sometimes referred to as the subcutis - expands and contracts during locomotion to act as both a shock absorber and a pump for blood flow.

Illus. 2.18 shows a foot where one claw has been removed to expose the underlying corium. The papillary corium can be clearly seen as the stippled area below the coronary band; the laminar corium is the lower part that resembles the gills of a fish, and the digital cushion is the protrusion of tissue below the heel.

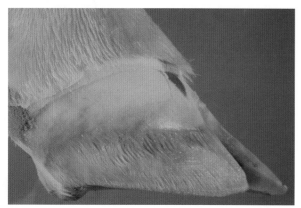

2.18 The stippled upper area is papillary corium, and the lower 'fish gill' appearance is laminar corium *(P.Ossent)*

The corium totally lines the inside of the hoof, as shown in Illus. 2.2, 2.3, 2.4 and 2.6. Towards the coronary band it is modified to form the finger-like projections known as papillae which penetrate like pegs into the overlying horn. The epidermis covering these papillae is the basic structure which produces the horn of the hoof. The blood vessels of the corium carry the nutrients required for horn formation.

Further down the wall, below the layer of the papillae, the corium is modified to form the leaves of the laminae. These interdigitate with the corresponding lamellae of the hoof to provide a tough suspensory system to support the body weight of the cow. Internally, the pedal bone is also suspended from laminar structures. Note that there are no laminae on the sole. Laminae are present only on the wall of the hoof, and there is a greater area of laminar attachment on the abaxial (outer) wall than on the axial wall. This is shown in Illus. 2.14 and 2.15. The reduced attachment of the pedal bone on the medial aspect (Illus. 2.15) has been suggested as a cause of slight rotation of the bone during locomotion, and this may contribute to the development of sole ulcers. The position of the white line running along the lower edge of the laminae of the axial wall is shown as a line in Illus. 2.15.

Digital cushion

At the heel, the corium is impregnated with fat, fibrous and elastic tissue to form the digital cushion. Small areas of yellow elastic tissue can be seen in Illus. 2.7 and the protrusion of the digital cushion t the heel can be seen in Illus. 2.18. The digital cushion acts as an extremely important shock absorber during weight-bearing and locomotion. As the foot makes contact with the ground there is an initial braking force exerted between the pedal bone and its suspensory laminae and then a slight movement of pedal bone at the heel, leading to compression of the digital cushion (96). Being covered by the flexible heel horn, the cushion can be compressed, thus preventing jarring of the skeleton. When no longer weight-bearing, it returns to its original shape. Further detail of the digital cushion is given in the next section on the pedal bone.

Maintenance of adequate blood flow within the foot is an extremely important part of horn production and yet when the animal's weight is borne by its feet, blood flow through the foot can be difficult. There are three main mechanisms involved:

- The digital cushion acts as a pump to suck blood out of the foot and force it back into circulation. In the hind foot especially, the heel – sole junction at zone 3 of the abaxial wall (Illus. 5.5) makes contact with the ground first and this initiates the pumping action. Clearly, lack of exercise would impede circulation.
- The minute blood vessels (the capillaries) in the corium expand and contract by muscle action as weight is borne by the feet. This muscle activity is destroyed by toxins and other changes associated with laminitis/coriosis.
- There are by-pass mechanisms, known as arteriovenous shunts, which, when weight bearing occurs, enable blood to circulate across the top of the foot, rather than through the capillaries of the corium. However, when the corium has been damaged by laminitis (especially in horses) the shunt may remain open too long, leading to pooling of blood in the capillaries, poor oxygenation of the tissues and consequently poor horn formation.

THE BONES AND ASSOCIATED STRUCTURES

The third tissue, deep within the foot, is the pedal bone and associated structures.

Pedal bone

The major bone of the bovine foot is the pedal bone, equivalent to the very last bone in our fingertip (Illus. 2.2), and is technically referred to as the third phalangeal bone. The pedal bone fits well forward in the hoof, being separated from the horn at the toe by quite a thin layer of corium. Laminae are more numerous over the anterior (front) and abaxial (outer) walls of the hoof and hence the pedal bone is essentially suspended within the hoof at these points. This 'tight fit' towards the toe is clearly shown in Illus. 2.3 and the area where the bone attaches to the lamellae of the abaxial wall can be seen in Illus. 2.9. In this picture the bone is resting on the floor of the hoof. In the living specimen it would be

suspended at a higher level, as shown in Illus. 2.4.

When the cow walks there is therefore relatively little movement of the pedal bone at the toe and on the abaxial wall, but posteriorly towards the heel and also axially towards the interdigital cleft the amount of movement is greater. This slight axial rotation during locomotion may be involved in the pathogenesis of sole ulcers, and will be referred to in a later section.

The pedal bone only extends to about three-quarters of the distance to the heel and the rear edge of the pedal bone sits almost directly above the sole ulcer site, as can be seen in Illus. 2.7 and in the boiled-out specimen in Illus. 2.9. The abaxial edge of the bone is flat, whereas the axial edge is arched, as shown in Illus. 2.19. The projection at the rear end of the bone (as indicated by the forceps on Illus. 2.20) is known as the flexor tuberosity, because this is

2.19 A boiled-out specimen showing the pedal bone with the arch on the axial aspect. Excess weight on the rear edge of the pedal bone could lead to bruising or a sole ulcer.

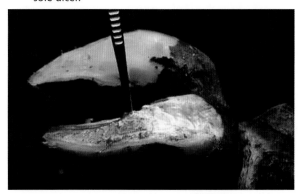

2.20 Note how the pedal bone protrudes into the sole.

where the flexor tendon attaches. This is shown on Illus. 2.23.

The above section describes how the front edge of the pedal bone is suspended by attachments to the laminar corium. The posterior (rear) edge is suspended by a ligament forming a hammock, known as the pedal suspensory apparatus, as shown in Illus. 2.21. The abaxial end (i.e. from the outer wall) of the ligament originates from the laminar corium while the axial ligament joins other ligaments in the area. Within this ligament are three pads of fat acting as shock absorbers, like the cushions in the heels of running shoes (66), although in older cows and cows that have had previous bouts of laminitis/coriosis, the fat starts to degenerate. This can reduce the effective suspension of the bone, and predisposes to sole ulcers. These changes are shown in Illus. 2.22.

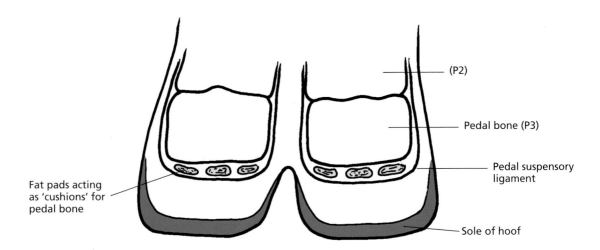

2.21 The pedal suspensory ligament is attached to the corium on the lateral aspect of the hoof, and to axial ligaments internally. Note the three fat pads acting as 'cushions' within the ligament.

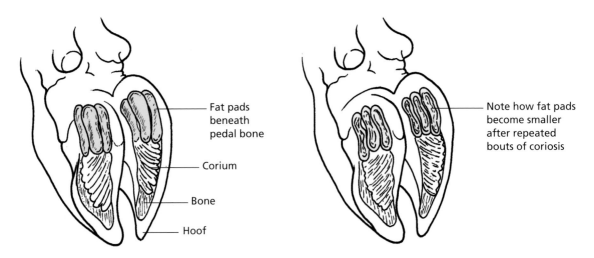

2.22 Detail of the fat pads acting as cushions within the suspensory ligament. After repeated bouts of coriosis the fat pads start to degenerate, as shown on the foot on the right. (Ossent and Lischer)

There are proposed differences in pedal bone suspension between the medial (inner) and lateral claws. In the lateral (outer) claw the pedal bone rests partly on the sole, while in the medial claw it is more tightly attached to the wall and thus exerts less pressure on the sole when weight-bearing *(58)*. This could be one reason why there is a higher proportion of sole ulcers in the lateral claws of hind feet. It is also the reason why the lateral claw should be left slightly longer when claw trimming. If both claws are trimmed to the same size, there is a risk that the lateral claw will be left with an excessively thin sole.

Tendons

Bending the leg forwards and backwards is achieved by tendons, one end of which is attached to a muscle and the other end to a bone. When a muscle contracts, it shortens and, via the tendon, it pulls and

moves the bone. There are two major tendons in the foot. The extensor tendon, which is attached to the top of the pedal bone (Illus. 2.23) *extends* the joints of the leg and helps to pull the leg forwards. The flexor tendon, which is attached to the flexor tuberosity at the base of the pedal bone, pulls the leg back and *flexes* the foot.

As tendons are also involved in weight-bearing and act as shock absorbers, they must be very strong. The thick, glistening white flexor tendon can be seen in Illus. 2.2. It runs down the back of the leg in an enclosed lubricated sheath (the tendon sheath) and attaches to the rear edge and base of the pedal bone.

Navicular bone

Where the tendon changes direction within the heel bulb, there is another small bone, the

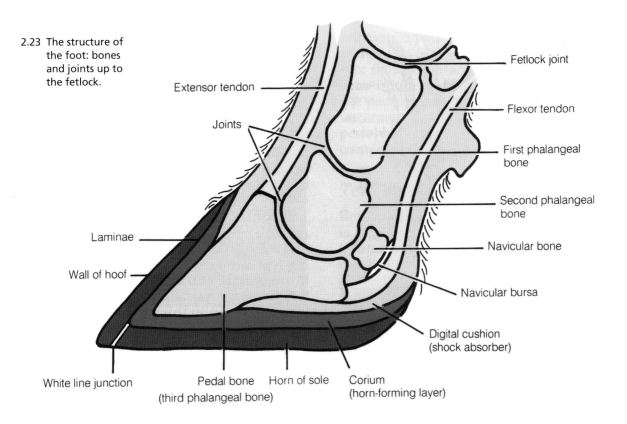

2.23 The structure of the foot: bones and joints up to the fetlock.

Extensor tendon

Joints

Laminae

Wall of hoof

White line junction

Pedal bone (third phalangeal bone)

Horn of sole

Corium (horn-forming layer)

Fetlock joint

Flexor tendon

First phalangeal bone

Second phalangeal bone

Navicular bone

Navicular bursa

Digital cushion (shock absorber)

navicular (sometimes called the distal sesamoid) bone, which facilitates movement of the tendon. This is shown in Illus. 2.24 and 2.25.

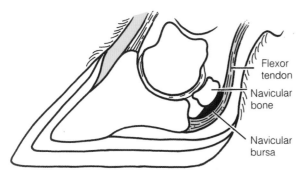

2.24 Position of the navicular bone, navicular bursa and flexor tendon.

2.25 A hoof showing the pedal bone and navicular bone in situ.

Navicular bursa

A lubricated area, a small pouch known as the navicular bursa (Illus. 2.24), lies between the tendon and the bone, and allows easy movement between the two structures. Note how the sole ulcer site is immediately below the point of insertion of the flexor tendon onto the pedal bone (Illus 2.23). If the ulcer penetrates deep into the corium, small white or creamy white strands of fibrous material are sometimes seen. These are fragments of the degenerating flexor tendon. Deeper penetration of infection from an ulcer can produce an abscess in the navicular bursa, sometimes referred to as a retro-articular abscess because it lies behind the joint. Affected cows will have an enlarged, inflamed and very painful heel

area, with reddening of the overlying skin (see Illus. 5.26). Lameness will be intense. Often a small bead of pus can be seen discharging from the ulcer site, an indication that there is an abscess beneath with considerably more pus present.

The only treatment for such cases is drainage through a radical opening of the abscess (14). Advanced or untreated cases may lead to infection of the navicular bone, to infection penetrating the pedal joint, or even to degeneration of the pedal bone itself, when amputation of the digit may be necessary. It is therefore important to treat retro-articular abscesses aggressively from the outset.

Pedal joint

The pedal joint is the junction of the pedal bone and the second phalangeal bone. The structure of a joint allows one cartilage-lubricated surface of a bone to move against the adjacent bone while both are taking weight. Any degeneration of the cartilage (i.e. arthritis) will produce severe pain on movement.

The nomenclature of the bones and joints up to the fetlock is shown in Illus. 2.23 and this can also be seen in Illus. 2.7. Note how the rear edge of the navicular bursa and the front edge of the navicular bone are incorporated into the pedal joint. Infection in this area can cause serious damage. Hence it is important to treat lame animals promptly.

LAMINITIS/CORIOSIS AND THE PATHOGENESIS OF HOOF DISORDERS

This section describes the changes that occur within the foot to produce hoof disorders such as sole ulcers and white line disease. There are two parts to the description of hoof disorders:

- *Pathogenesis*, the changes that occur within the foot to produce the hoof defects.
- *Aetiology*, the on-farm factors that produce the changes within the foot.

The aetiology of the disorders, that is the on-farm factors that lead to the changes within the foot, are described in Chapter Six.

Earlier in this chapter we saw how the stratum germinativum, the layer of cells of the epidermis covering the papillae, was the site of horn formation. By continuous multiplication, large squame (thin, plate-like) cells are slowly pushed away from the stratum germinativum. Keratin synthesised within their cytoplasm forms strengthening keratin fibres and as the cells shrink, dehydrate and die, they produce the very hard horn surface which we know as the outer wall of the hoof. The corium 'feeds' the germinal epithelium, hence any disruption in the corium will lead to a disruption in horn formation. Put another way, a healthy corium produces a healthy hoof, whereas a diseased corium often leads to hoof defects.

Laminitis simply means inflammation of the laminae, although in effect all areas of the corium, and not just the laminae, are likely to be congested and inflamed. The term 'laminitis' is commonly used (as in the following text) to include a generalised inflammation of the corium. Probably the terms coriitis or coriosis would be more appropriate, simply indicating a dysfunction of the corium. This dysfunction can be seen in several different forms.

- Increased blood flow through the corium means that horn is produced more rapidly. This can lead to overgrowth of the wall or sole and may also result in less mature and therefore softer and less durable horn reaching the wearing surfaces. Like a tree, more rapid growth leads to softer tissue. These changes are particularly prominent in the white line area.

- Damage to the vascular system (blood vessels) can lead to the release of serum or even whole blood cells. These fill the spaces between the squame cells, and are seen in the hoof as blood mixed with horn in the sole or white line area. Illus. 2.13 and 2.26 are good examples.

- In some instances the blood vessels in the corium become so badly dilated that blood flow almost stops, leading to 'sludging'. Lack of blood flow means that the tissues become anoxic (starved of oxygen), no nutrients are available for the production of new hoof, and waste products from the surrounding tissues accumulate because there is no blood flow to remove them. Horn growth may then totally cease.

2.26 A sole haemorrhage. Note blood at the toe and at the white line. The right claw has diffuse discoloration throughout.

There is no one single cause of disruption of the corium and subsequent poor hoof production. The main factors affecting the corium are thought to be:

- physical trauma
- metabolic changes within the cow, such as those that occur during pregnancy and early lactation
- toxins, for example from the gut (e.g. rumen acidosis) food or from disease.

Trauma

One cause of inflammation of the corium is simple physical bruising. A similar syndrome occurs when we damage our own fingernail, as shown in Illus. 2.27. In this instance, trauma leads to immediate haemorrhage, and if the bleeding is severe, nail production is totally disrupted. As the new nail starts to grow again, we can see a line across it, as in Illus. 2.28. Eventually the damaged nail is shed from the tip of our finger (Illus. 2.29) and we once again have healthy horn (nail) tissue present. These changes can be seen easily in the fingernail because it is thin. However, when haemorrhage occurs within the sole it cannot be seen from the outside. The damaged tissue will grow through the sole at 5mm per month until it eventually reaches the outer surface, as in Illus. 2.13. As the sole is 10-15 mm thick, the haemorrhage may not be seen until two to three months after the initial trauma.

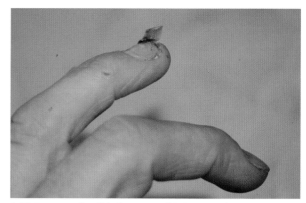

2.29 Damaged nail being cast. This is equivalent to the sole ulcer stage in dairy cows.

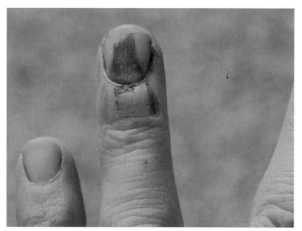

2.27 Trauma produces haemorrhage in the corium.

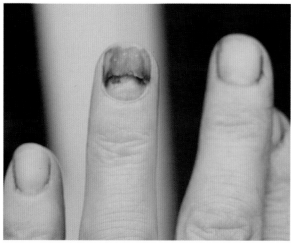

2.28 Damaged horn is slowly growing down across the fingernail.

One might ask why do we not see lameness as soon as the trauma occurs, rather than two months later? I was certainly aware of the trauma when it happened to my own finger in Illus. 2.27! In fact the cow does respond to the initial pain. Detailed studies (49, 3) have been able to demonstrate a reduction in milk yield between two and four months prior to the onset of lameness, i.e. when the bruising to the corium is first seen. Lameness is a later sign, and does not occur until the mixed blood and hoof have reached the bearing surface of the sole, bacteria have tracked back up through the damaged column of sole horn, reached the corium and produced pus and pressure. Of course, many haemorrhagic areas never develop into lameness. They simply grow out of the sole, as is shown in Illus. 5.15-5.17.

Illus. 2.30 shows how weight transmitted down the leg can cause pinching of the corium between the hard surfaces of the rear edge of the pedal bone above and the horn of the sole beneath. The shape of the pedal bone is clearly seen in Illus. 2.24. The lower edge of the bone is arch-shaped, especially on its axial (inner) surface. This is the point where its attachment to the hoof is minimal. Because there is a stronger laminar attachment to the abaxial (outer) wall than to the axial (inner) wall, during locomotion the bone rocks slightly from side to side, allowing the flexor tuberosity which protrudes from the lower border of the axial aspect of the bone to impact onto the corium. Illus. 2.20 shows a foot where the sole horn has been totally removed to demonstrate the way in which the flexor tuberosity is likely to be the main point of impact onto the corium. This is why during hoof trimming it is necessary to remove hoof in this area so that the sole stops bearing weight at this point.

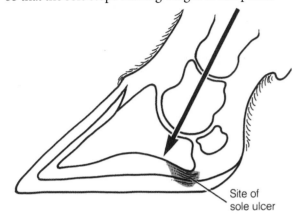

2.30 Weight passing down the leg will be partially transmitted on to the posterior (rear) edge of the pedal bone which could cause pinching and damage to the corium.

The pinching of the corium between pedal bone above and the hoof below damages the blood vessels and this can lead to the release of red blood cells. These are then mixed with new hoof as it is formed, and the mixture of blood and hoof grows down through the hoof to eventually reach to the surface of the sole. The haemorrhages in Illus. 2.13 and 2.26 are typical examples. In Illus 2.13 note the blood clots at the sole ulcer site (A), the white line (B) and in Illus. 2.26 at the toe, these being the front and rear contact points of the pedal bone with the solear hoof beneath. Such areas are often referred to as 'bruising'. It is a type of bruising, but of course the bruise developed some eight to twelve weeks earlier (horn grows at 5 mm per month and the sole is approximately 10–15 mm thick) and has only just appeared at the surface.

In some cows, you will find that paring away a few superficial slivers of horn removes the bloodstained area and leaves intact healthy horn beneath. In this instance, bruising must have taken place over a very limited period of time and there was a rapid return to healthy horn formation. In other animals (and usually over the sole ulcer site), the mixture of blood and horn is continuous from the external weight-bearing surface of the sole down to the corium, indicating that bruising is still occurring.

This would be like a column or tube of mixed concrete and sawdust passing down through an otherwise well-laid area of concrete. Once the cement surface is worn away and the concrete /sawdust mixture is exposed, water and debris would very quickly erode the concrete/sawdust mix leaving a deep cavity in the concrete. These changes are shown diagrammatically in Illus. 2.31.

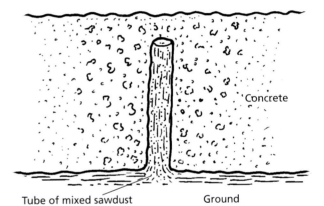

Tube of mixed sawdust and cement   Ground

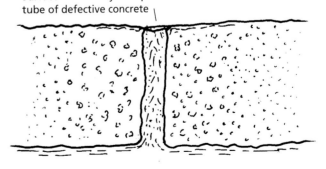

Surface worn away to expose tube of defective concrete

2.31 The column of mixed hoof and blood that may pass from the corium to the bearing surface of the sole can be compared to a column of sawdust mixed with cement coming up through concrete. When the surface of the concrete has been worn away (below) to expose the sawdust/cement mix, a hole rapidly develops.

When there is a continuous column of blood and poor-quality horn stretching from the corium to the sole it is very easy for bacteria to penetrate. Once the bacteria reach the corium they have food, warmth and moisture, their three essential components for growth, and they then multiply to form pus. The pus increases the pressure within the foot, leading to pain and lameness. Even in the absence of infection, the presence of very poor quality horn (i.e. the mixture of blood and hoof) means that the cow does not have a good covering to her foot. If she stands on a stone the defective hoof will collapse under pressure and this will transmit pain to the corium. We experience similar effects ourselves if we try to walk over very rough ground in thin slippers!

Metabolic Changes

Calving can also disrupt horn production. Detailed changes in the white line of heifers before and after calving have been described by taking slivers of horn and examining them under the very high magnification of an electron microscope (69). Healthy elongated horn leaflet cells and rounded interdigitating cells are shown in Illus. 2.16 and 2.17. Note how the cell junctions are firmly fixed together, giving strength to the horn. After calving, the horn began to degenerate in almost all the heifers. This was seen initially as a separation of the squame cells (Illus. 2.32), the spaces between them becoming filled with red blood cells, bacteria and general amorphous debris. These changes will clearly weaken the overall strength of the horn.

The worst-affected cells were very badly damaged. There were large spaces between them, cell membranes were disrupted and, in some, keratinisation had been so badly disturbed that there was a complete absence of keratin fibres within the cell and the cells degenerated (Illus. 2.33).

The net effect of these processes is a serious weakening of the structure of the hoof, thus allowing impaction of debris or penetration of grit, stones or infection into the corium. The changes

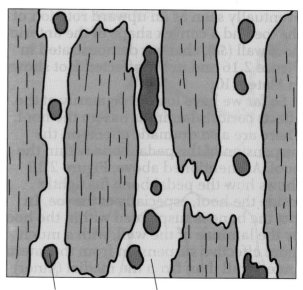

Red blood cell   Intercellular space filled with serum

2.32 Section of white line in a heifer after calving. The spaces between the squame cells have been enlarged and become filled with serum, red blood cells, bacteria and general debris. *(D. Logue and S. Kempson)*

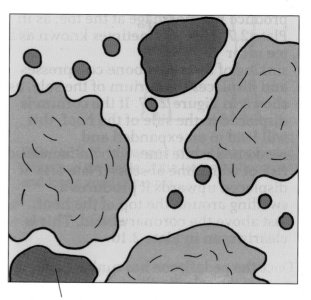

Degenerating squame cell

2.33 Advance changes in white line horn. The squame cells are degenerating. There is little or no internal keratin, and the intercellular spaces are large, filled with blood, serum and accumulations of amorphous debris. *(D. Logue and S. Kempson)*

described are, of course, microscopic, requiring magnification of many thousands to appreciate their detail. On the hoof itself the same changes are seen as a yellow discolouration of the hoof or white line, as on the sole in Illus 2.13 and 2.26. This is due to blood vessels damaged by laminitis/coriosis, allowing yellow serum to ooze into the spaces between the horn cells.

Toxins and Diet

The precise way in which endotoxins produce changes in the corium are still not clear. Endotoxins from bacteria can be involved, and the injection of endotoxin can have a dramatic effect on blood pressure within the foot in both the live animal and in perfused limb experiments. The effects may therefore be simply the result of changes in blood pressure as described above. Other potential toxic substances include histamine, lactic acid (from rumen acidosis), and serotonin. Rumen acidosis is commonly believed to be an important factor, in that it leads to an increase in the amount of rumenal lactic acid, increases endotoxin production by *Streptococcus bovis*, and increases histamine production by the bacterium *Allisonella histaminiformans*. Absorption of histamine from the rumen is greater under conditions of low rumen pH. Rumen acidosis also depresses biotin synthesis, and biotin is an important component of hoof horn. This is discussed in more detail in Chapter Six.

Illus. 5.38 shows a horizontal fissure running around the front of the hoof. This cow had been very ill with a coliform mastitis immediately after calving. Although she eventually recovered, the total interruption of horn formation, followed by resumption days or weeks later, led to two separate parts to the hoof. The lower 'thimble' should eventually grow off the end of the toe (Illus. 5.39). Less severe attacks of coriosis/laminitis lead to grooves around the hoof, as seen in Illus. 2.34 and 5.40. These have been referred to as 'hardship lines' *(50)*. A series of parallel horizontal grooves indicates that the cow suffered repeated attacks of disruption of the corium.

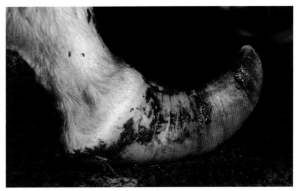
2.34 Chronic laminitis. Note that the overgrown toe no longer makes contact with the ground during walking and that the anterior wall is concave.

The soft, powdery pockets of white horn, which may be found on the sole (Illus. 2.35), are sometimes said to be a consequence of laminitis. This is not correct. The powdery material is simply old and degenerating superficial sole horn not removed by natural wear, probably because (as in Illus. 2.35) the wall is higher than the sole and hence the sole has not been subjected to friction.

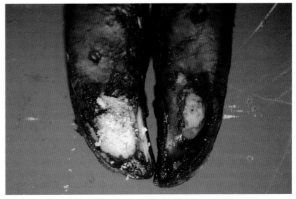
2.35 Pockets of soft powdery horn on the sole have been attributed to laminitis, but this material is normal sole horn which has not been worn away.

Changes in Pedal Bone Suspension

So far we have looked primarily at the effects that coriosis/laminitis has on the hoof. There are also dramatic effects on the suspension of the pedal bone within the hoof. As mentioned above, Illus. 2.23 and 2.36 show how the pedal bone fits tightly inside the hoof, especially at the toe. In fact, the

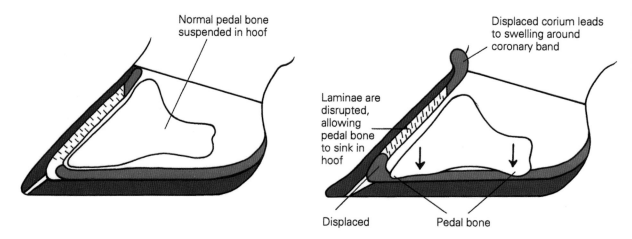

Normal pedal bone suspended in hoof

Displaced corium leads to swelling around coronary band

Laminae are disrupted, allowing pedal bone to sink in hoof

Displaced

Pedal bone

2.36 Laminitis can disrupt the suspension of the pedal bone, allowing the bone to sink onto the corium of the sole. The corium may then become displaced laterally, leading to an enlarged white line, or upwards, producing swelling above the coronary band. *(Dr P. Ossent)*

bone is suspended within the hoof by the laminae of the wall, with a much more effective suspension from the lateral (outer) wall than from the medial (inner) wall (Illus. 2.15). The suspension is by means of filaments of fibrous tissue, like the filaments of two feathers held side by side, as shown in Illus. 2.37. Enzymes called metallomatrix proteinases (MMPs) are able to vary the 'tightness' of the attachment of the pedal bone to the laminar corium, and hence to alter the flexibility of the whole suspensory system.

In Illus. 2.37(i) the MMP molecules are small and round, and are holding the pedal bone close to the hoof wall. In Illus. 2.37(ii) the molecules have elongated, and this allows the leaves of the laminae to move apart, thus loosening the connection between the pedal bone and the hoof wall. MMPs are activated by changes in hormones such as 'relaxin' and 'hoofase' around the time of calving and this increases the amount of movement of the pedal bone, leading to an increased susceptibility to 'bruising'. Endotoxin produced in the rumen by *Streptococcus bovis* is also said to have a 'loosening' effect on the pedal bone. However, if a heifer or cow suffers a severe disruption of the corium, then the MMP-controlled suspensory system breaks down and the bone 'sinks' within the hoof,

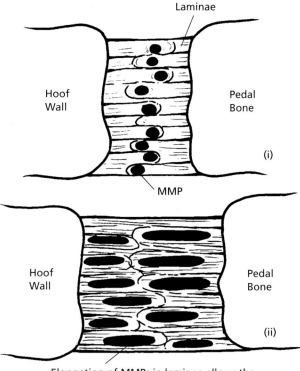

Laminae

Hoof Wall

Pedal Bone

MMP

(i)

Hoof Wall

Pedal Bone

(ii)

Elongation of MMPs in laminae allows the pedal bone to move away from the hoof wall

2.37 The pedal bone is attached to the hoof wall by a filamentous suspensory apparatus, like two feathers side by side. MMP (Metallomatrix proteinases) enzymes control the degree of flexibility of the system, and when they elongate this increases the degree of movement of the bone within the hoof.

dropping onto the corium of the sole (Illus. 2.36). This can have several effects:

- If the rear end of the pedal bone drops, the corium becomes pinched at this point and a sole ulcer may be produced (see Illus. 2.30 and 2.13).

- If the front edge drops, this will produce haemorrhage at the toe, as in Illus. 2.26. This is sometimes known as a toe ulcer.

- Sinking of the pedal bone may compress and displace the corium of the sole to the side of the hoof, leading to an expanded and weakened

white line, with an increased risk of white line abscess, as shown in Illus 2.36.

- If the corium is displaced upwards, it produces a swelling around the top of the hoof, just above the coronary band. This is clearly seen in Illus. 2.34. Swelling around the coronary band is often seen in tender-footed cows after calving and is associated with such changes.

- Engorgement and enlargement of blood vessels associated with laminitis/coriosis in such a confined area lead to pain and discomfort. The

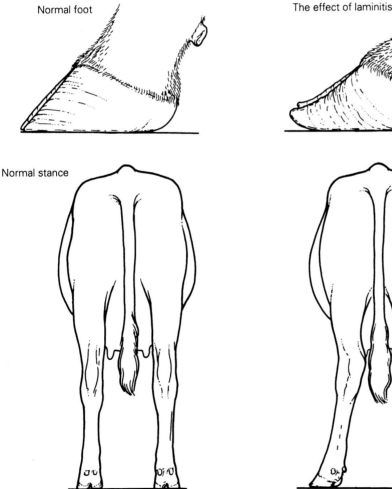
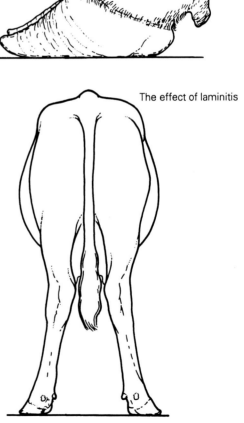

Normal foot

The effect of laminitis

Normal stance

The effect of laminitis

2.38 Changes in hoof shape and stance due to laminitis. The toe lifts off the ground, the heel drops and the angle of the front wall becomes much shallower. Affected cows walk with hocks together and toes turned outwards.

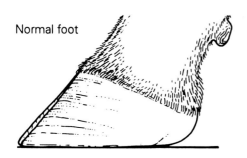

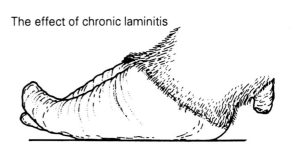

2.39   Chronic laminitis: a sunken heel, concave front wall and toe rotated upwards.

affected cow tries to take the weight off her toes by walking on her heels and by turning her toes outwards. This decreases the height of the heel, makes the angle of the front wall more shallow and causes the cow to walk with her hocks closer together. These changes are shown in Illus. 2.38 and in the stance of an affected cow in the Frontispiece.

- The longer-term effects of coriosis/laminitis may eventually be seen as an upward rotation of the toe and a convex shape of the anterior hoof wall *(96)*, changes demonstrated in Illus. 2.39 and in the affected foot shown in Illus. 2.34.

Once the pedal bone has sunk onto the corium of the sole, it will never regain its original position, and the affected animal will have to walk in discomfort from a compressed corium for the remainder of her life. This can lead to permanent poor horn formation, particularly around the sole ulcer site, and hence an increased susceptibility to sole ulcers and white line defects. In some cows the pedal bone will have dropped so much that its rear edge can be palpated just beneath the sole.

In summary, therefore, generalised inflammation of the corium (coriosis), and this includes laminitis, may lead to any one of the following changes:

- Pain and discomfort, especially at the toe, encouraging the cow to walk back on her heels.
- Upward rotation of the toe, leading to a concave 'dishing' of the anterior (front) hoof wall and gross claw overgrowth.
- Disruption of horn growth, seen as hardship lines, which are horizontal grooves encircling the wall, or even a complete horizontal fissure.
- Conversely, increased blood flow within the corium may stimulate increased growth of poorer quality, i.e. softer, horn.
- Yellow (serum) discolouration of the sole horn, and in more advanced cases blood in the white line and sole ulcer site.
- Sinking of the pedal bone, leading to displacement of the corium both to the side of the hoof (expanding and weakening the white line) and above the coronary band (producing a swelling above the hoof).

CHAPTER THREE

Weight-bearing Surfaces and Hoof Overgrowth

The primary objective of hoof trimming is to restore the foot to its correct shape and weight-bearing surfaces. As such it is essential that there is first a thorough understanding of the normal foot and of the changes in hoof shape, structure and dimension which can occur with overgrowth.

WEIGHT-BEARING SURFACES

In a correctly shaped hoof, weight is taken on the heel and on the wall. As shown in Illus. 3.1, the wall runs abaxially along the outside of the claw to the toe and then axially from the toe posteriorly along the first third of the interdigital space. It is, unfortunately, common to see the axial wall removed during foot trimming. This is because the axial wall is easier to trim than the abaxial wall, and because some say that there should be a big gap between the claws at the toe. This is not correct. If you remove the axial wall you will destabilise the claw and allow it to roll over, leading to hoof deformities.

Illus. 3.2 shows the claw of a heifer that has just come in from pasture. Note how the wall is well above the surface of the sole, and how the sole would only become weight bearing if the foot sunk into the soil. In commercial production, because many animals are housed at least partly on concrete, the wall becomes worn down to sole level and we often think that a flat sole is the norm. This is probably not the case, however, and if it were possible to trim a foot so that the wall was left slightly higher than the sole then it is likely that this would be a good option. The more commonly seen flat sole means that weight is also taken, albeit to a lesser extent, on the white line area and 10–20 mm of sole adjacent to it. This is shown in Illus 3.1 *(42, 51, 91, 96)*. (If you are

3.1 The weight-bearing surfaces of the foot, indicated by shaded areas.

3.2 In grazing heifers the wall is higher than the sole and is the major weight-bearing surface.

unsure of the terms being used, refer back to the explanations in Illus. 2.1.)

At the toe almost the whole area of the sole becomes weight-bearing, with weight being taken equally on the axial and abaxial walls. The unshaded area of sole on the diagram should not be bearing weight as this is the sole ulcer site, with the flexor tuberosity of the pedal bone immediately above. The wall and sole should be flat from the heel to the toe, making even and consistent contact with the ground surface

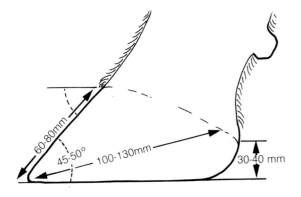

60-80mm
45-50°
100-130mm
30-40 mm

3.3   Approximate angles and dimensions of a normal claw.

throughout and thereby maximising weight bearing. The front angle of each claw should be quite steep, around 45 degrees (Illus. 3.3), with the toe making firm contact with the ground during locomotion *(32, 96)*. This was something that was very clear over 2,500 years ago, as can be seen from Illus. 3.4, which is the foot of a bull from the city of Persepolis in Iran!

An axial view of a single claw, viewed from the interdigital space (Illus. 3.5 and 3.6) clearly shows how the wall runs posteriorly for the first third only (i.e. the weight-bearing area) and then gradually merges with the sole.

The remainder of the axial surface of the claw, running back to the heel, consists of a concave area of sole (unshaded in Illus. 3.1). This area should be kept clear and open, and forms the interdigital space between the two claws. In a normal hind foot, *slightly* more weight is taken on the lateral rather than the medial claw, as the lateral claw is slightly longer *(80)*. This difference is shown in Illus 3.1 where, on the medial claw, the axial wall particularly is smaller.

Illus 3.7 shows a cross-section of two claws from

3.4   The foot of this 2,500-year-old bull from Persepolis shows the correct angle and weight-bearing surface.

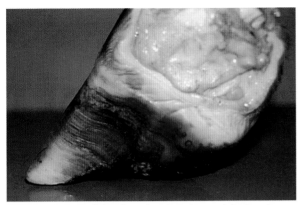

3.5 Axial view of the claw showing that weight bearing should be on the first third of the wall and heel only.

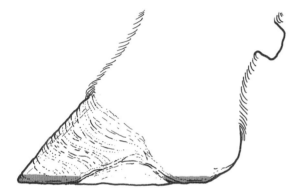

3.6 Axial (inner) view of a single claw, to show solar concavity, with weight bearing at the heel plus the first third of the axial wall.

a 14-month-old Friesian steer. Note how, even at this age, the lateral claw (right) is significantly bigger than the medial claw, although the medial claw has the thicker sole. (This difference becomes accentuated with overgrowth.) Hence, if an attempt were made to trim the lateral claw down to the same size as the medial claw, the sole of the lateral claw could become too thin, and lameness could result. This has been shown to occur experimentally by several authors *(97a)*.

To optimise the efficiency of weight bearing within the foot, the anterior wall, from toe to coronary band, should be at an angle of 45–50 degrees with the horizontal, as in Illus. 2.5 and 3.5. Provided that the anterior wall is straight, then of course the angle of the toe will be identical (45–50 degrees, see Illus 3.3).

The length of the anterior wall, often referred to as the toe length, or sometimes as the length of the dorsal border, should be 75–85 mm, with the coronary band sloping slightly backwards, forming a shallow angle with the horizontal. The anterior wall angle is, of course, determined by the height of the heel, which should be approximately 25–35 mm for young cows and 30–45 mm for older animals. However, these are average values only and, as one might expect, there is considerable variation

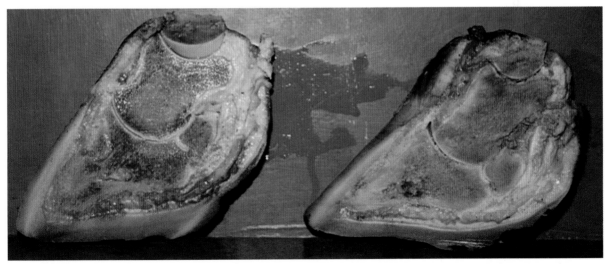

3.7 Sections of outer (lateral) and inner (medial) claws of a 14-month-old Friesian steer. Note the thicker sole on the lateral claw.

in claw dimensions between animals *(7, 74, 85)*. This variation is associated with factors such as the following:

- Breed: Jerseys will obviously have smaller claws than Friesians or beef breeds.
- Age: first-lactation heifers have smaller claws than cows, adult size being reached by approximately the third lactation.
- The differences between front and hind feet.
- Individual variation within a breed: some individual cows have abnormally large and/or shallow feet.

If in doubt its better to leave the claw slightly long. You can cause serious lameness by over-trimming, but either no effect or just mild discomfort by under-trimming

Many hoof conformation factors have a high heritability; in other words they are highly likely to be passed on to the next generation. Cows with long claws and shallow heels for example, as in Illus 3.8, will produce offspring with similar defects. In the hind foot the angle of the toe has a particularly high heritability *(7)*, so ideally you should not breed from cows with shallow hoof angles. It has been shown *(85)* that bulls with long toes and large soles are more prone to sole ulcers than other bulls and this influence could be passed on to their progeny.

Conversely, foot trimming, that is the restoration of the foot to a 'normal' shape, has been shown to improve the gait and locomotion score of cows quite quickly *(72)* (Table 6.5, p.122). When compared with untrimmed controls, the incidence of lameness also decreased. Hoof trimming is therefore important, both economically and for the welfare of the cow.

As we have studied the dimensions of a normal foot, we can now examine where overgrowth occurs.

HOOF OVERGROWTH

There are three main areas of overgrowth, namely the toe, the lateral claw and the sole, particularly of the lateral claw, and this leads to a disparity between the size of the two claws. Although all three occur simultaneously, it makes understanding easier if they are considered separately.

Overgrowth at the Toe

The shape of the hoof at any one time is a balance between the rate of growth and the rate of wear:

Hoof shape = growth minus wear

There is a range of factors that influence growth, while other factors influence wear. The balance between the two at any one time will determine hoof shape and size.

Examples are given in the following table.

The overall balance is quite complex, because often the same factors stimulate both growth and

3.8   Cows with very long toes and very shallow heels are best not retained for breeding.

Factors increasing hoof growth	Factors increasing hoof wear
Level of feeding	Rough surfaces under foot
Age (younger animals have faster growth)	Wet conditions (leading to soft hoof)
Trauma (stimulates growth)	Excess standing and/or walking
Inflammation (stimulates growth)	Soft horn

wear. For example, rough uneven surfaces will increase the rate of hoof wear. At the same time the rough surfaces will increase trauma to the underlying corium and this in turn stimulates the rate of horn growth. However, because the horn is produced more quickly it will be softer and hence more liable to be worn away.

Although the whole hoof grows at the same rate, the rate of wear will vary, because different parts of the hoof are softer than others. The wall at the toe is the hardest part of the foot. This is because:

- The wall has more reinforcing tubules, 80 per sq mm versus 20 per sq mm in the sole.

- The wall at the toe is the oldest part of the hoof, around sixteen months old, whereas the wall at the heel is only seven to eight months old.

- The wall runs around the toe, thus giving two segments of wall with only a small central segment of sole (Illus. 3.1).

Hence, although the whole foot may be growing at the same rate, wear is generally greatest at the heel and least at the toe. The net result is that overgrowth occurs primarily at the toe. This has the effect of slowly reducing the angle of the toe from 45 to 40 to 35 degrees.

The slope of the coronary band increases and the depth of the heel decreases. These changes are shown in Illus. 3.9. In extreme cases of overgrowth (e.g. Illus. 3.10), the anterior hoof wall becomes concave and the toe deviates upwards (Illus. 2.34). Because there is then no longer contact between the toe and the ground, no wear occurs at the toe and overgrowth continues unchecked.

Dishing of the anterior hoof wall is probably also an effect of laminitis *(96)*. It is the wall that is primarily affected by overgrowth and hence there is often greater overgrowth on the abaxial (outer) side than on the axial (inner) side of the foot. This is because the wall extends axially for only one-third of the distance along the interdigital cleft. The overall effect of this is often seen as a rolling of the wall under the sole, as demonstrated in Illus. 3.11 and 3.12.

In addition to these external changes in hoof shape, there are dramatic changes occurring within the hoof. To walk in comfort, the cow needs to have her pedal bone within the foot sloped towards the toe, as shown in Illus. 3.13. Hence, if it were possible, when her toe overgrew she would walk with her heel in the air, as shown in Illus. 3.14. Clearly, this is not possible, and as her heel drops in relation to her toe (Illus. 3.15), the pedal bone rotates backwards and starts to pinch the corium towards the heel. This is clearly seen in Illus. 3.15. Even simple claw overgrowth can be a predisposing factor for a sole ulcer, therefore. Note

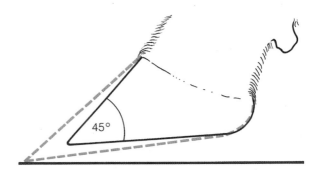

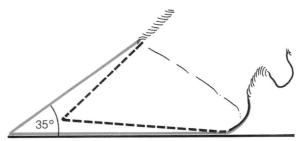

3.9   Hoof overgrowth occurs primarily at the toe.

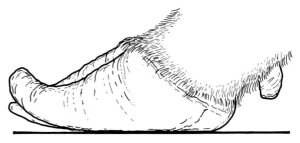

3.10 More advanced overgrowth, leading to a concave anterior wall and a toe which does not touch the ground.

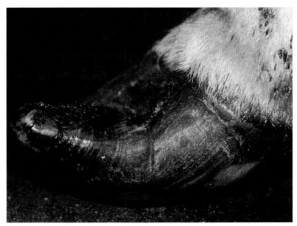

3.11 An overgrown foot. Note how the toe no longer makes contact with the ground; the front wall is concave and the lateral wall rolls under the sole.

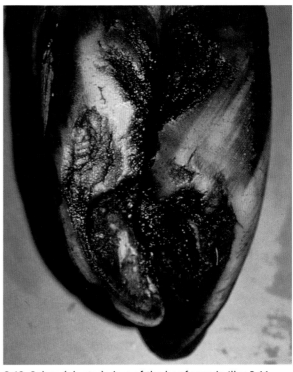

3.12 Solear (plantar) view of the hoof seen in Illus 3.11. Note how the wall has extended across the sole to make the sole ulcer site a weight-bearing area.

the changing angle of the lower edge of the pedal bone in Illus 3.13. Illus. 3.16 shows a cross-section of an overgrown foot with gross excess of horn at the toe. The foot has been tipped forward onto its toe for photographing, but when walking, this cow would be well back on her heels with the toe raised.

Slurry heel makes the situation worse. Erosion of the heel exacerbates the backward rotation of the foot and pedal bone. If the posterior edge of the pedal bone lies immediately above the edge of the eroded sole, the sole could bend at this point during weight-bearing, further exacerbating the

backward rotation of the pedal bone and discomfort within the foot, as seen in Illus. 5.20. These changes are shown diagrammatically in Illus. 3.17.

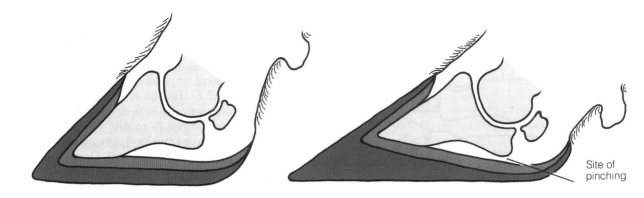

Site of pinching

3.13 Overgrowth at the toe leads to a backward rotation of the pedal bone and pinching of the corium between the pedal bone and hoof.

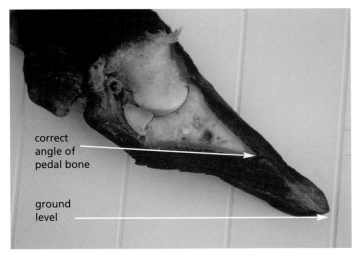

3.14 Ideally the cow would stand with her heel raised, keeping the pedal bone at the correct angle.

correct angle of pedal bone

ground level

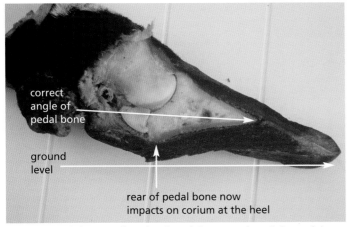

correct angle of pedal bone

ground level

rear of pedal bone now impacts on corium at the heel

3.15 The heel drops to floor level, and the rear edge of the pedal bone pinches the corium.

3.16 A section of overgrown hoof (left) compared with a normal hoof (right). Note the excess horn at the toe and backward rotation of the pedal bone.

Although it is still suspended within the anterior hoof at the toe, the backward rotation of the pedal bone leads to more weight being taken along its posterior edge, i.e. towards the heel. During weight bearing and locomotion this can produce a pinching of the corium between the pedal bone above and the sole of the hoof below, as shown in Illus. 3.13.

Pinching of sensitive tissues leads to pain; hence a cow walking on her heels because of overgrown toes may walk with considerable discomfort. We have all seen such animals, shuffling along with dropped pasterns and fetlocks close to the ground. The syndrome is less pronounced in the medial claw, because the pedal bone has a more effective suspension within the inner claw (96). Hence, affected cows tend to walk by throwing their lateral claws outwards, trying to take weight off the lateral claw and transfer more weight onto the medial claw, as shown in Illus. 2.38 and 3.18.

In Chapter Two we discussed the importance of pinching of the solear corium and how that can lead to bleeding and subsequent sole ulcers (see page 26). Correct hoof trimming is therefore an important part of the prevention of sole ulcers.

The importance of overgrowth at the toe has been demonstrated experimentally (91).

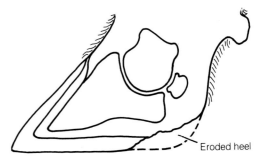

Eroded heel

3.17 Erosion of the heel can further destabilise the foot. Note how the eroded heel may extend as far forwards as the rear edge of the pedal bone.

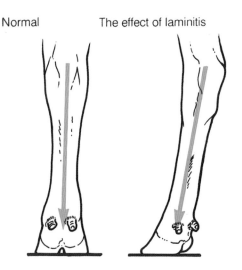

Normal   The effect of laminitis

3.18 Changes in hoof shape and stance due to chronic laminitis.

Fixing a wedge of wood to the sole at the toe increases the degree of flexion of the pedal joint. This in turn puts stress on the sole which becomes stretched, especially at the sole – heel junction immediately below the rear edge of the pedal bone. In the experiment it was found that within a few weeks the sole was grossly thicker than the control

claw and there were early changes indicating the start of the formation of a sole ulcer. Mild trauma may cause irritation of the sole corium and the production of sole overgrowth (Illus. 3.19). More severe trauma and stretching may cause permanent damage to the corium and result in a sole ulcer (91).

Overgrowth of the Sole

Overgrowth of solear horn occurs on the lateral claw of hind feet and, to a lesser extent, on the medial claw of front feet. It is seen as a ledge of horn growing from the sole and protruding axially into the interdigital cleft (Illus. 3.19 and 3.20). The sole overgrowth may be so pronounced that it becomes the major weight-bearing surface of the foot (Illus. 3.19), and of course this point is immediately below the posterior edge of the pedal bone.

It has been proposed that the overgrowth occurs because, when the cow is walking on concrete, her hoof wall becomes worn away, her sole then becomes more weight bearing, and the flexor tuberosity of the pedal bone impacts more frequently on the corium. This stimulates the

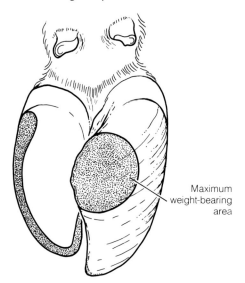

Maximum weight-bearing area

3.19 Overgrowth of solear horn is common on the lateral claws of hind feet. The shaded area now becomes weight-bearing. (Compare this with the correct weight-bearing surfaces in Illus 3.1.)

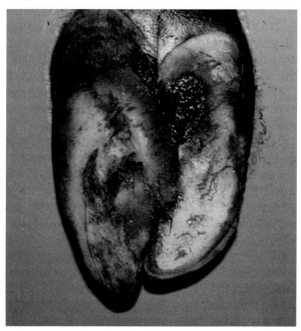

3.20 An overgrowth of solar horn.

growth of additional sole and produces the sole ledge. But, of course, at the same time the ledge itself increases the chances of the corium being pinched during locomotion.

When the ledge is removed during hoof trimming, there is often an area of pin-point bleeding or even frank haemorrhage into the horn at this point. It is interesting that on front feet it is the inner claw which becomes larger and this is where the solar overgrowth occurs. It is also, unfortunately, the inner claw on front feet that most commonly develops sole ulcers.

Disparity of Claw Size

The third part of hoof overgrowth is seen as a disparity in hoof size. Several reasons have already been given for the fact that the lateral (outer) claws of hind feet become larger than the medial. For example:

- Poorer suspension of the pedal bone within the hoof in the lateral, compared with the medial, claw leads to increased pinching of the corium.

- Because the outer claw is naturally longer, it takes more trauma during walking and this stimulates overgrowth.

- There is a tendency for cows to stand with their hocks together and feet turned outwards, particularly following overgrowth at the toe.

Even when hooves have been correctly trimmed it is the lateral hind claw that takes the maximum amount of weight (98). This increased weight bearing stimulates the growth of additional horn and further exacerbates the overload.

By measuring the amount of weight taken on each claw during standing and locomotion, it has been cleverly demonstrated that there is a much greater variation in the amount of weight taken on the outer claw, compared to the weight variation on the inner claw (96). For example, when the cow is standing still and upright, weight is taken almost evenly on both claws of both hind feet (Illus. 3.21) – although recent research has shown that in fact a

bit more weight is taken on the lateral than the medial claw. As her weight is being transferred from her left onto her right leg, weight is taken particularly onto the outer claw, until the left leg is lifted off the ground. During the transfer process the weight on the lateral claw reaches 80 per cent of the total. Hence, the lateral weight variation is zero to 80 per cent, whereas the medial claw weight variation is only zero to 50 per cent. The same process then occurs when the left leg takes weight and the right leg is lifted off the ground.

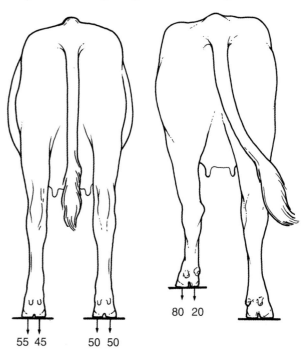

3.21 As the cow changes its weight from one foot to another there is much greater variation in the weight taken on the outer claw than the variation in the weight-bearing of the inner claw. This could be another reason why there is overgrowth of the outer claw on hind feet.

This increased variability of weight bearing on the lateral (outer) claw leads to contusions (bruising) and exostoses (small bony growths) on the pedal bone of that claw similar to the changes seen in Illus. 5.21 (96). These lesions lead to further pain, once again encouraging the cow to swing her legs out while walking and thus transfer more

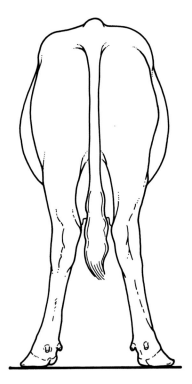

3.22   An overgrowth of the lateral claw.

Other factors that may play a part include engorgement of the udder and metabolic changes leading to laminitis (coriosis) at the time of calving. With an engorged and slightly painful udder, the periparturient cow will tend to walk by throwing her hind legs outwards in an arc-shaped swinging movement and she may stand with her legs slightly further apart. The outer claw would then make slightly less contact with the ground, would be worn less and hence overgrowth could occur. By mid-lactation, when the udder has decreased in size, the lateral claws may already be overgrown and hence the cow continues to stand splay-legged. Udder size is unlikely to be a major factor, however.

A further factor is simply standing on concrete. When a cow stands on a slippery surface she does the same as us – she moves her legs apart to maintain her balance and stop herself from slipping. As she walks on concrete she may continue to swing her legs in an arc movement described above, thus increasing the disparity of claw size.

The cumulative effects of all these processes is to produce hoof overgrowth and discomfort in the feet, especially in the lateral hind claws. Foot trimming aims to reverse these processes and is an attempt to compensate for the adverse effects of management, housing, feeding and breeding to which cows are subjected.

weight onto the medial (inner) claw. Both chronic low-grade inflammation of the foot and an abnormal gait can lead to overgrowth of the lateral claw (a common feature in many dairy cows), thereby further destabilising the foot. This is demonstrated in Illus. 3.22.

CHAPTER FOUR

Hoof Trimming

EQUIPMENT NEEDED

A variety of tools and equipment is available for hoof trimming. A selection is shown in Illus. 4.1 This does not mean that alternatives are not equally as good. Each individual trimmer must decide what suits him or her best.

4.1 Equipment for hoof-trimming: clippers, double-edged knife, file.

Knives and clippers

A double-edged hoof knife is probably the most convenient to use. Alternatively have two knives, one for forward cutting and one for reverse. However, this entails changing knives each time a change in the direction of cutting is required and since I often do a few forward strokes followed by a few reverse strokes I find the procedure of changing knives exasperating.

Whatever the knife, it is important that it is sharp. Personally I find that a rotating strip of emery cloth is the best for sharpening the main blade. With the cloth strip rotating away from you,

run the knife edge across the strip so that a constant angle is obtained for approximately 25 per cent across the width of the blade down to its edge. If the angle is too steep, i.e. the knife is sharpened too close to its edge, the knife loses its edge too quickly. Finish by buffing the knife on a wheel.

A chainsaw file is small enough to get into the hook at the end of the knife and hence is very convenient The sharpened knife can be protected during transit by wrapping it in a cloth, or inserting it into an old milking machine liner.

When hoof trimming, and especially when searching the foot for pus tracks, it is best to cut with the flat blade of the knife, as shown in Illus. 4.2. If only the curved tip is used, it is much more difficult to identify lesions in the hoof, and paring takes much longer.

4.2 Hold the knife with both hands and cut with the flat. Push down and across to give a sawing action.

The knife should not simply be pushed vertically downward through the hoof. Think of using a hoof knife as if you are cutting a loaf of bread. You do not push the knife through the bread, you use the knife *at an angle* and with a sawing action. By moving the blade across the hoof (i.e. from left to right as you look at Illus. 4.2) at the same time as pushing towards the toe, a sawing action is achieved and this will make cutting very much easier. On a particularly hard foot (e.g. during a dry summer), keeping the blade wet also helps.

Personally, I find that standing behind the cow, facing backwards and sometimes with the foot resting on my knee, is the best position for trimming. This is shown in Illus. 4.3. If you hold the knife in both hands and push downwards to cut, much of the cutting force originates from your shoulders. In addition, it is a good position from which to visualise the claws and thereby achieve a balanced and correct weight-bearing foot at the end of trimming.

However, some operators prefer to stand facing the claw and cut by pulling the knife towards them.

A variety of clippers can be used for removing the horn from the toe (Illus. 4.1). I now use the type on

4.3 The position preferred for foot trimming: behind the cow, facing backwards, with the cow's foot on the trimmer's knee.

the left in the photograph, although the larger ones in the centre have the advantage that they cut off much larger lengths of toe in one bite. Others favour hoof shears as a method of removing large amounts in one cut.

A surform or coarse file will assist with tidying the edges and sharp corners of the hoof when trimming has been completed. A file run over the bottom of the foot after trimming also makes sure that there is continual contact between the hoof wall and the ground surface from heel to toe, thus maximising weight bearing. Similarly, the file can check that the axial and abaxial walls at the toe are correct and of equal height.

Protective gloves are a must if large numbers of feet are to be trimmed. They allow greater force to be applied to the knife and help to prevent the knife slipping when it gets wet or dirty. You only have to see how quickly a pair of cloth gloves wears through when foot trimming, to realise how much damage there must be to your hands! Protective armbands (not shown) also make life easier. They protect your forearm from the effects of scratching as your arm passes over the end of the hoof

Power tools

Electrical grinding and cutting instruments are needed if large numbers of cows are to be trimmed, but it is important that you have first correctly learnt how to trim a foot with a knife. A common danger of electrical devices is that, unless they are used in skilled hands, excess hoof may be removed or the sole may be left excessively flat. Final trimming and shaping should ideally be done with a knife.

I have even seen electric cutting discs used to remove the outer wall of the hoof, making the cow's foot look small and 'pretty'. This can be a very dangerous action. If the wall is removed to the extent that weight bearing is taken on the softer structures of the sole and white line, this can lead to excessively rapid hoof wear after trimming, thin soles and severe lameness.

It has been suggested that some grinding devices

lead to overheating of the horn, with subsequent damage and hoof weakening, but trials have shown that this is unlikely (63).

RESTRAINT OF THE COW

Once again, this is very much a question of personal choice. Provided that the cow is restrained and supported so that she cannot struggle excessively or damage herself, and provided that the foot is sufficiently well restrained to avoid injury to the operator, but allows good, clear access for trimming, then the precise methods of restraint are not important.

I have very limited personal experience of roll-over tables. I find that the foot is not in the most accessible position for trimming and that it is more difficult to visualise the correct shape. Furthermore, I do not like the way in which some cows slump to the ground when they are released from the crush. On the other hand, I can see that if there are large numbers of feet to be trimmed, then anything that makes the job easier must be worth considering.

In stand-up crushes and chutes belly-bands support the cow well, but they take time to apply and, in some cases, the cow hangs limp and has to be lowered to the floor before release.

However, for front feet a single band placed immediately behind the front legs to support the chest provides excellent restraint, and with the band in position the cow will stand much more quietly. Make sure that the band is placed well foward under her front legs, with the overhead support ideally running back from above her neck region and certainly not from over her chest. If the belly band is able to slip back to behind her rib cage it will cause discomfort and often makes the cow take all four feet off the ground. She is then left hanging in the belt and may be difficult to release.

Winches used to raise hind legs should have a secure self-locking mechanism and either a

large wheel or a slow screw to turn for lifting. I have seen several frayed tempers and damaged hands when a struggling cow has inadvertently released a winch mechanism!

When using ropes I favour the system shown in Illus 4.4. A rope is placed just above the hock, using a slip-knot which tightens during lifting, thus discouraging struggling. The rope is wrapped round a side bar of the crush and back around the hock for a second time, before returning to the same side bar of the crush. This produces a 'pulley' mechanism.

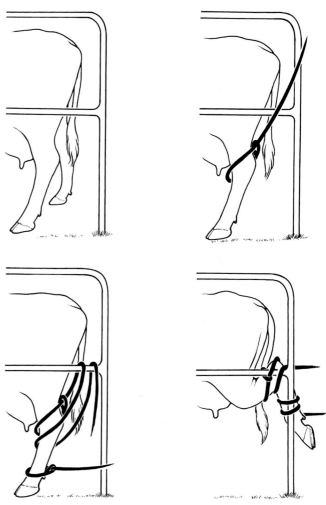

4.4   A system of two ropes to lift the hind leg of the cow and tie the fetlocks securely to the vertical bar at the rear of the crush.

A second rope is attached around the fetlock. Pulling back on this second rope will make the cow kick slightly, thus lifting her leg. By pulling the first rope at the same time, the leg is lifted. The hock is secured to and level with the horizontal crush bar and the fetlock is fixed to the vertical. The cow is held firmly, thus reducing struggling, and yet she is well supported to reduce the chances of her falling in the crush. This system works best with two operators.

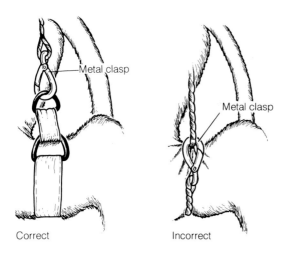

Correct   Incorrect

4.5   Do not use the metal clasp on the end of the lifting rope around the cow's hock. A strip of belting (below) or a short loop of rope will provide much greater cow comfort and encourage her to stand still.

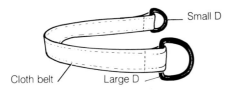

Small D

Cloth belt   Large D

If a winch is used, **make sure** that the metal clasp on the end of the rope does not cut into the cow's leg. (This happens all too often.) A short length of 50 mm wide belting, with a metal 'D' at each end, one larger than the other as shown in Illus. 4.5, is ideal. The belt is placed around the hock, the small D slips through the larger D and

the metal clasp is then clipped to the small D.

A small loop of rope is a simple alternative to the belt, and opinions vary as to whether to use the belt as a 'lasso', as in Illus. 4.5, or as a sling. Some say that if the leg is just supported in a sling, i.e. the large loop and the small loop are both attached to the metal clasp, then the rope does not cut into the skin as much as it might, and the cow would stand more quietly.

A similar system, but using one rope only, is the *Pepper Footrope* shown in Illus. 4.6-4.8. It consists of a leg strap, a supple rope, with a shackle at one end, and a jamming cleat set into the rope a short distance from the shackle. The ropes used should be moderately thick for both operator and cow comfort.

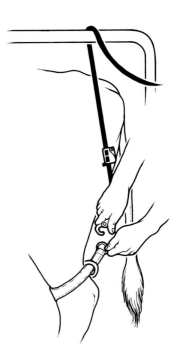

4.6   Secure the cow in a crush or standing, and lay the rope over the top bar or a beam. Place the leg strap around the hind leg, above the hock, by passing the smaller metal ring through the larger one. Attach the rope to the leg strap with the shackle. *(D. Pepper)*

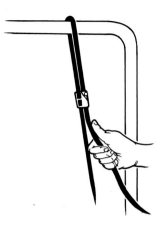

4.7 Thread the free end of the rope through the cleat, inside the guide, and down through the jamming part. Pulling gently downwards on the rope will take up the slack without putting any tension on the leg. *(D. Pepper)*

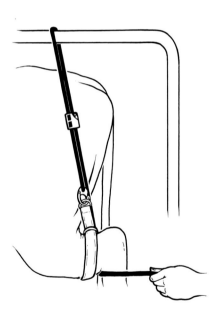

4.8 Pass the rope around the inside of the leg, and tug sharply from behind at a safe distance. When the cow kicks, keep the tension on the rope so that the leg is held by the cleat in each new position. Having achieved the most comfortable height for the cow and operator, secure the leg to any convenient upright using the long end of the rope. *(D. Pepper)*

HOOF-TRIMMING TECHNIQUE

The objective of hoof trimming is to restore the foot to its normal shape and weight-bearing surfaces. In order to understand this procedure, it is important to read Chapters Two and Three first, which describe the normal hoof and what happens during hoof overgrowth. Many different methods of hoof trimming have been described, and they are all trying to achieve the same final result, namely the restoration of normal weight-bearing surfaces and a reduction in the development of hoof defects.

The method I am now going to describe has been divided into four stages, although in reality one stage merges with and constitutes part of the next stage, as the feet are slowly brought back into shape.

Cut One

Cut the overgrown toe back to its correct length, i.e. approximately 75 to 85 mm from the coronary band to the toe (Illus. 4.9). This is approximately one hand-breadth. Place the thumb on the heel and the palm of the hand with the fingers not quite touching each other on the abaxial (outer) wall of the lateral claw. With the first finger penetrating well into the top of the interdigital space at the front of the foot, the toe should be cut off in line with the little finger.

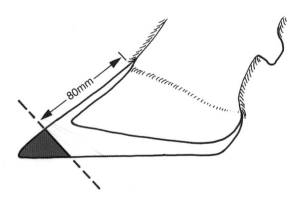

4.9 Cut One – cut the toe back to the correct length, approximately 80 mm or one generous span of your palm.

The width required is a good palm span, and be generous: i.e. it is always better to leave slightly more rather than cut off too much. There is, of course, considerable variation in 'natural' claw shape (see Chapter Three). The distance described can only be approximate, therefore, and each cow must, to a certain extent, be assessed as an individual.

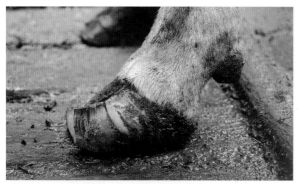

4.10   A square-ended toe after Cut One.

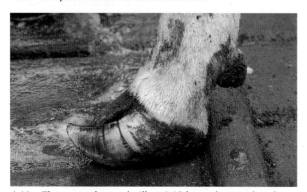

4.11   The same claw as in Illus. 4.10 but prior to trimming.

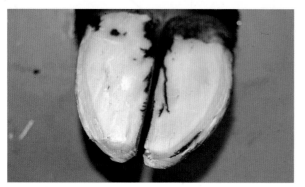

4.12   The white line at the toe can no longer be seen on the surface of the sole, but it is visible across the cut end.

Cut One can be made at right angles to the anterior wall, rather than at right angles to the sole, as this will reduce the amount of cutting required at Cut Two, although the difference is not too important.

After Cut One, the foot is left with a square-ended toe, as shown in Illus. 4.10. Compare this with Illus. 4.11 which is the same claw before trimming. Illus. 4.12 is a close-up of a cut toe. Note how at the toe the white line can no longer be seen on the sole, but is visible on the cut edge. Although the hoof is now the correct length, the toe is still too high (Illus. 4.10) and the pedal bone remains rotated backwards towards the heel. Absence of the white line at the toe indicates that weight cannot be fully transmitted along the wall.

Cut Two

Draw a line from 'A', the top of Cut One, to 'B', the bottom of the heel and remove all the hoof from beneath this line, the shaded area in Illus. 4.13. Much of this will consist of removing horn from the toe. Provided that Cut One is in the correct position, there is no danger of penetrating the sole, although as trimming progresses the thickness of the sole should be repeatedly checked by applying pressure with the thumb in the toe area. As soon as any softening or 'give' is detected, further trimming must be discontinued. This can happen if Cut One is made too short, as demonstrated in Illus. 4.14. Cut Two would now penetrate the sole.

Another common error is shown in Illus. 4.15.

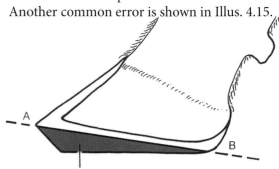

Repeatedly check the thickness of the sole in this area

4.13 Cut Two – remove excess horn, particularly from the toe, so that the anterior wall is brought back up towards the 45-degree norm.

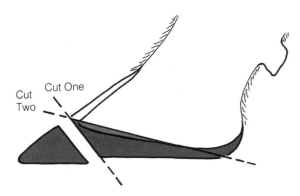

4.14 Cut One was made too short. Cut Two would now penetrate the quick (the corium) at the toe.

Cut One is cut too short and, to avoid penetrating the sole, the toe is left square-ended. This means that the wall at the toe is no longer a weight-bearing surface and that it is the sole at this point which becomes weight-bearing. This could lead to bruising of the sole and discomfort for the cow.

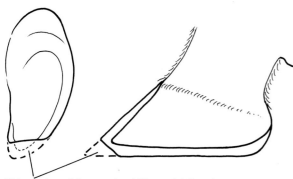

This section of the toe should be weightbearing

4.15 Cut One was again too short so that the toe was left square-ended. Weight cannot now be transferred onto the wall at the toe.

Provided that Cut One is in the correct position, trimming off excess horn for Cut Two will slowly make the white line reappear on the sole, until it is once again visible running around the toe. This is shown in Illus. 4.16 which is the same foot as in Illus. 4.10 and 4.11, but with Cut Two completed.

Removal of horn from the toe has the effect of bringing the wall of the hoof back up to a more

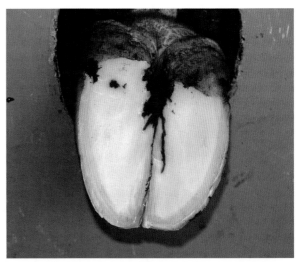

4.16 Cut Two. By trimming excess sole from the toe, the white line with the wall outside slowly reappears.

upright angle, i.e. back to the correct 45 degrees as shown in Illus. 4.17. At the toe the weight bearing has once again been transferred to the wall, and the pedal bone has been tilted forwards, thus reducing possible pinching action by its rear edge. In Illus. 4.16, which should be compared with Illus. 4.12, the white line has reappeared at the toe.

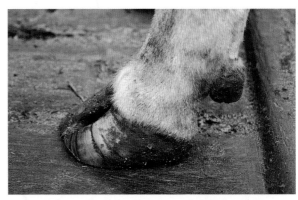

4.17 Hoof-trimming complete. Note the much steeper angle of the front wall of the hoof. The toe is slightly off the ground, partly because the cow is standing in the crush with her leg forward.

Cut Two can often be made with foot clippers, especially the smaller hoof nippers shown on the left of Illus. 4.1. Start at the toe and slowly work back towards the heel, taking off a progressively narrower piece of horn with each clip, so that by the time you get towards the heel the cut has finished and you are left with a wedge-shaped piece of horn that has been removed. This has the effect of removing horn at the toe and thus returning the foot to a better angle.

Illus. 4.18, 4.19 and 4.20 demonstrate Cuts One and Two on a transverse section of hoof. Note how in Illus. 4.18 there is a considerable overgrowth at the toe but the heel is of normal height and this rotates the pedal bone backwards.

4.18 An overgrown claw. Note the excess horn at the toe.

4.19 The overgrown claw in Illus. 4.18 after Cut One. The wall and white line area at the toe no longer make contact with the ground.

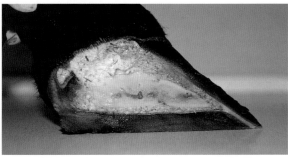

4.20 The claw following Cut Two. Normal weight-bearing surfaces have been restored.

After Cut One (Illus. 4.11) the wall and white line at the toe no longer make contact with the ground surface, i.e. they are no longer weight bearing. Cut Two returns the toe to a weight-bearing position and rotates the pedal bone forwards (Illus. 4.20). The anterior wall of the hoof adopts a more acute angle. Some foot-trimmers leave a 5 mm step at the toe when trimming cows prior to entering winter housing, thus allowing for growth at the toe. I can see no advantage in this, and I am not aware of seeing a cow's foot with a 5 mm step occur naturally.

Take care when trimming the heel. Often the heel does not need any horn removing from it, and in fact to do so could be counter productive. This is because removing horn from the heel simply rotates the foot backwards and this decreases the angle of the front wall, undoing part of the good that has been achieved by the first stages of the trimming. If the horn of the heel is badly pitted it may be necessary to remove a few of the larger fissures, but in most instances small lesions of 'slurry heel' are best left and treated by foot bathing (see later sections).

Cut Three

Stage three consists firstly of removing any ledge of solear overgrowth from the lateral claw (or medial front claw) as seen, for example, in Illus. 3.20. Also at this stage the soles of both claws are 'dished' to produce a concave surface over the central sole ulcer area (Illus. 4.21) so that it does not bear weight.

This increases the space between the digits, making interdigital impaction by foreign bodies and dirt less likely and possibly reducing the incidence of foul and interdigital skin hyperplasia (also known as 'corns', 'growths' or 'tylomas'). Also known as interdigital fibromas, growths should be correctly called interdigital skin hyperplasia, since they are an overgrowth of skin. Providing additional space between the claws reduces the pinching action on these growths and will often lead to their spontaneous resolution.

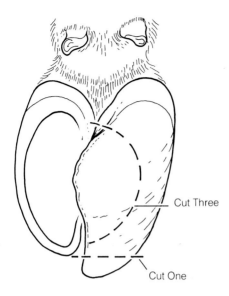
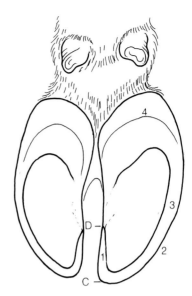

4.21 Cut Three – remove any overgrowth of the sole so that weight-bearing is returned to the correct surfaces and specifically not to the sole ulcer area.

Dishing the hoof to produce a concave sole applies to the mid-third of the sole only. The axial wall ('C–D', Illus. 4.21) running posteriorly for the first third of the distance from the toe must not be removed. It is an important weight-bearing surface and should be at the same height as the adjacent abaxial wall.

When trimming is complete, points 1, 2, 3 and 4 on Illus. 4.21 should all be of equal height; that is, on the same level in a horizontal plane.

Removal of the axial wall is a common mistake made by many farmers and herdsmen. The theory that the toes should not be touching when trimming is complete is not correct. If the axial wall is removed, the claw becomes seriously destabilised, because it is only supported by one edge. Removal of excess axial wall can also lead to penetration of the corium at this point and, on more than one occasion, I have seen cows seriously lame because of over-zealous trimming in this area. Those unfortunate cases of white line abscesses and under-run sole which do involve the axial wall almost always produce severe lameness and are slow to heal.

Illus. 4.22 shows two single claws placed in a weight-bearing position. The claw on the left has retained its axial wall and so remains upright. In the claw on the right the axial wall has been removed and hence for this claw to become weight bearing it will rotate until its axial wall has made contact with the ground surface. The rotation of the claw on the right is very clearly demonstrated.

4.22 The claw on the left has retained its axial wall and remains upright. The claw on the right tilts because its axial wall has been removed.

Cut Four

Overgrowth of the lateral hind claw, compared to the medial, is commonplace in dairy cows. The reasons are given on page 41. The fourth stage of hoof trimming (Illus. 4.23) consists of removing additional horn from the lateral claw so that it becomes roughly equal in size to the medial claw. This effect can be best appreciated by referring to Illus. 2.38 and by comparing Illus. 4.11 and 4.17, which show a claw before and after trimming.

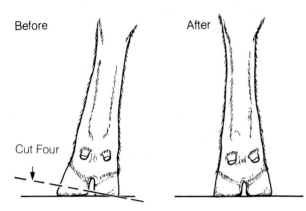

4.23 Cut Four – trim the outer and inner claws to an even size (left), thus bringing the legs and stance of the cow back into an upright position (right). This normally involves trimming additional horn off the lateral claw in hind feet and the medial claw in front feet.

Do not trim the two claws to exactly the same size. Experiments have shown that if you do this, the sole of the lateral claw will be too thin, and this can lead to brusing of the corium and subsequent lameness *(80)*. The lateral claw should be left slightly longer.

Cut Four is one of the few occasions when heel horn can be removed, but even then it should be done with caution and ensuring that an equal thickness of horn is removed from the heel to the toe. Removal of excessive heel horn could have the effect of tipping the anterior hoof wall away from the 45 degree angle, thus lifting the toe and rotating the pedal bone backwards to where pinching of the corium might occur.

However, if there are loose flaps of badly under-run heel horn these may have to be removed, to allow penetration of the foot-bath solution.

In a proportion of cows with severely overgrown and neglected claws it may not be possible to correct defects fully in one trimming session. This applies particularly to cases of coriosis/laminitis where the anterior wall has become concave, as in Illus. 2.34. Two or three attempts over a period of nine to eighteen months may be needed to restore chronically rotated digits to the correct stance, and in some cases the flexor tendon will have been so badly stretched that they will never fully return to normal.

GENERAL CONSIDERATIONS and WHEN TO TRIM

Unfortunately, hoof trimming is not a one-off task. Although trimming will undoubtedly improve foot conformation, gait and cow comfort, those cows which walked badly before trimming will probably have some internal defect of the corium and/or pedal bone and will therefore develop overgrown feet in less time than the other cows in the herd. This is particularly so if some of the errors of management, feeding and housing discussed in Chapter Six are not rectified. Footcare is therefore an on-going process, similar to measures a herdsman must take to control mastitis.

I believe that footcare is the herdsman's task and, like many other tasks, refresher courses are beneficial. There are occasions when additional (veterinary) advice is needed. Routine foot trimming has been shown both to decrease the incidence of lameness and to improve the gait, locomotion score and therefore welfare of the cows *(32, 72)*. Excessive foot trimming can be deleterious, however, especially in situations where soft soles can be a problem *(48)*.

One theory of hoof trimming recommends that it is advisable first to trim the medial claw to the correct shape, and then use this as a template for trimming the lateral claw. Whilst this system may have its merits, it is my opinion that it is not always a correct course of action, and especially when dealing with lame cows. This is because it is often beneficial on welfare grounds to leave the sound (often the medial) claw slightly larger than normal in order to increase its weight-bearing potential when there is a lesion in the opposite (often the lateral) claw.

When to Trim

When is the best time to trim? Once again there are no set guidelines, but as a general rule feet should be *examined*:

- When lame or showing discomfort in walking.
- When there is serious hoof overgrowth present. This is often best detected as cows are walking out of a herring-bone parlour, when both the sides of the hoof and any potential solear ledge can be seen.
- Other farms lift and examine all feet at 2 – 3 months after calving to remove any solear overgrowth.
- At drying-off.

The advantages of lifting feet at the **drying-off stage** are that:

- Accumulated hoof overgrowth from the stresses of calving and lactation can be removed.
- As lameness is most frequent and has the greatest economic effect in early to mid-lactation, feet need to be in ideal condition prior to calving.

- In occasional cows where trimming has been over-zealous, producing slightly soft soles, cows turned out to pasture at drying-off have ample time to recover.

Perhaps at drying-off it would be better to think of **examining** of all feet rather than trimming. Many cows simply do not need to have the toe shortened, and just removing a few slivers of horn from the sole to check for impaction of the white line is all that is required. Dogmatic insistence that all toes must be clipped at drying-off is not only using unneccessary time, but it may also be deleterious to the cow in that either the toe is left 'square-ended' and does not bear weight correctly, or the sole is left excessively thin and soft.

It is counter-productive to leave feet in an overgrown state for excessive periods of time. Cows such as the one shown in Illus. 2.34 will develop stretched tendons and simply continue to walk badly even though they may have been trimmed correctly.

CHAPTER FIVE

Common Diseases of the Foot and their Treatments

Before discussing the various housing, nutritional and management factors associated with the prevention of lameness, it is clearly important to have some idea of the common lesions causing lameness and their treatment. A 'lesion' is simply a term used to describe a pathological change, or a disorder, in a tissue, in this instance in the foot. Some aspects of treatment can be carried out by trained farm staff, but other treatments need expert veterinary attention. Whenever in doubt, call for veterinary assistance. A cow is far too valuable to take chances with. In addition to welfare considerations, a wrong decision could result in much more expensive treatment later, or even the total loss of the cow.

The majority of the lesions causing lameness are in the foot, and by far the most common lesions are sole ulcers, white line defects, digital dermatitis and 'foul'. The incidence of the different conditions is given in Chapter One. In this chapter I describe the various lesions causing lameness and give an approach to treatment. The lesions are divided as follows:

- **hoof conditions** such as sole haemorrhage, white line defects, sole ulcers, heel ulcers and toe ulcers, foreign body penetration, horizontal and vertical fissures, toe necrosis and slurry heel.
- **bone conditions,** i.e. disorders of the pedal and navicular bones.
- **skin conditions** such as interdigital skin hyperplasia ('growths' or 'corns'), and the infectious disorders of digital dermatitis, interdigital necrobacillosis ('foul') and mud fever.

HOOF CONDITIONS

Sole Haemorrhage

Sole haemorrhage is not really a syndrome in itself, but rather part of the overall process of laminitis/coriosis that leads to the production of other hoof defects; in other words sole haemorrhage often precedes the formation of white line defects and sole ulcers. It is only included here as a separate item for ease of reference. The pathogenesis (formation) of haemorrhage in the sole was dealt with in detail in Chapter Two, especially Illus. 2.20 and 2.27-2.29. Haemorrhagic areas, combined with softening and/or yellow discolouration of the horn, may occur in other parts of the sole in addition to the ulcer sites, and may occur either with or without an ulcer or white line defect. Typical examples are seen in Illus. 2.13 and 2.26. The yellow discoloration of the horn is the result of serum 'ooze' from the corium, as described in Chapter Two.

These changes are generally associated with an increased frequency of other diseases of the digit and have sometimes been termed the subclinical laminitis syndrome, SLS (50). However, other researchers who have carried out a detailed microscopic examination of these changes state that although there is loss of onychogenic substance (horn forming tissue), inflammation (laminitis) is **not** involved. Presumably this is partly because the haemorrhage occurs in areas of the sole where there are no laminae, but also because there is no inflammatory process present. There are numerous causes of sole haemorrhage – physical, metabolic, managemental and nutritional –which will be discussed in the next chapter.

Illus. 2.13 and 2.26 show acute sole haemorrhage, plus a sole ulcer, from a cow in a herd which was experiencing a serious lameness problem. The blood clot at the toe in Illus. 2.26 is likely to be the result of either trauma from the ground (such as standing on a stone, especially if the sole was thin), or from a failure of the pedal bone suspension (see Chapter Two), and a subsequent sinking of the bone within the foot. Both would result in pinching of the corium between the pedal bone above and the solear hoof beneath, and lead to bleeding. Haemorrhages at the toe are also seen occasionally in the front feet of working bulls, presumably due to trauma when dismounting from oestrous cows. These may also be referred to as toe ulcers (see p. 63).

White Line Disorders

The detailed structure of the white line and the effects of laminitis/coriosis weakening the horn in the area are discussed in Chapter Two, and this needs to be read before this section can be fully understood. Once the white line has been weakened, small fragments of dirt, or even quite large stones, especially if they have sharp edges, can penetrate. The most common points of entry are shown in Illus. 5.1. Abaxially and towards the heel (site 1) is the most common site because:

- This is the site where, during locomotion, there are the greatest sheer forces between the rigid hoof wall, the suspended pedal bone and the movement of the softer heel horn contracting and expanding over the digital cushion.

- It is also the point of maximum impact and weight bearing of the foot as it makes contact with the ground. The severity of these forces is increased if there is overgrowth at the toe, because the toe will be lifted and more pressure is then applied to the wall during locomotion.

- The horn is softer at this site, firstly because tubule density is lower, i.e. there are fewer tubules per square mm of horn, and second because the horn is younger and hence less mature than at the toe.

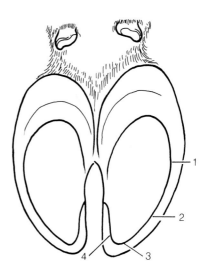

5.1 Common points of entry of infection in white line disease, given in increasing order of importance (1 to 4).

White line disease is commonly seen as a stone penetrating the white line, such as in Illus 5.2. The first reaction is that it is the stone which is the cause of the lameness but, of course this is not entirely true. The stone has only penetrated the foot because the white line was weak. If the white line cement were healthy, it is unlikely that the stone would have penetrated. However, once it is present the stone acts as a wedge, forcing the wall away from the sole and further expanding the white line.

Following impaction of the white line with dirt, or penetration by stones, there are two possible scenarios.

5.2 A stone penetrating a white line defect.

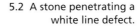

First, the continued growth of the hoof and white line may carry the debris to the surface, where it is worn away and eventually shed, leaving healthy horn beneath. Alternatively, further softening of the white line, or possibly standing on another stone, may force the material deeper into the hoof until it eventually reaches the corium (the quick). Such material will obviously be infected. The bacteria present will multiply, stimulating the defence mechanisms of the cow to produce pus. The pus accumulates, leading to increased pressure and it is this pressure that produces pain in the sensitive corium and therefore lameness.

It may not even be necessary for dirt to penetrate. If there is a small track of blood running through the white line from the corium to the sole surface, this may be a sufficient route of entry for bacteria to penetrate and cause an abscess. In other cases there may have been sufficient inflammation of the corium to produce 'sterile pus' which leads to an under-run sole and lameness.

Although dirt may have tracked in through the white line, the hoof often closes tightly around the track and it no longer remains a viable route for the pus to escape. As pus accumulates, therefore, it spreads progressively between the corium (covered by epidermis) and the overlying hoof, producing what we commonly refer to as 'under-run' horn.

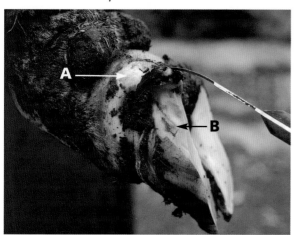

5.3 A white line abscess. Pus is breaking out through the softer perioplic horn at the heel at 'A'. 'B' is the original site of white line penetration.

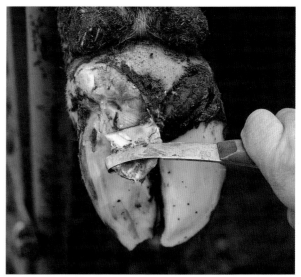

5.4 The extent of the under-run sole, all of which must be removed to promote healing.

This can be either under the sole (to produce an under-run sole) or under the wall.

The softer perioplic horn of the heel is more easily under-run and many white line abscesses take the line of least resistance and track under the soft horn of the heel to discharge at the coronary band above the heel. A typical example is shown in Illus. 5.3. Lifting of the heel horn (A) shows where pus is escaping. The original point of white line penetration (B) can also be seen. Illus. 5.4 shows the extent of the under-run horn, all of which must be removed if rapid healing is to be achieved.

White line disorders increase with age, with one study (54) showing that the incidence doubled at each parity. Heifers had two cases per hundred cows per year in their in first lactations; second calvers four cases/100 per year; third eight cases /100 per year, and fourth and above sixteen cases/100 cows per year. This is presumably associated with the deterioration of hoof quality with age.

Treatment

In the majority of cases, lameness caused by white line disease is effectively an abscess between the corium and the sole and, like any other abscess, drainage is vital to produce healing. The pinkish-white tissue beneath the sole in Illus 5.3 is corium covered by epidermis and this will form the new sole. If the under-run horn is carefully removed there should not be any significant bleeding, because bleeding only occurs when horn is detached from healthy corium. This balance is difficult to achieve, however, and sometimes a small area of healthy tissue is cut, leading to haemorrhage. A small amount of bleeding is of little significance and does not retard healing. As soon as the pressure of pus has been relieved there is usually a rapid reduction in the degree of the lameness. Note how the affected claw (the left one in Illus 5.4) has been trimmed short to minimise weight bearing.

Because the pedal bone is relatively tightly attached at the toe (Illus. 2.3), there is less room for the pus to expand in this area. Therefore white line infection at the toe (site 3 on Illus. 5.1 and zones 1 and 2 on Illus. 5.5), the axial wall (site 4, Illus. 5.1) or at the first third of the abaxial wall (site 2) will cause a more acute lameness. Site 4 can be particularly severe and slow to heal. Illus. 5.6 shows a small bead of pus draining from another white line penetration site. All under-run horn must be

removed (Illus. 5.7), exposing the corium covered by a thin layer of germinal epithelium. The initial point of entry of the infection can be seen as a small haemorrhagic area on the left of the picture.

5.6   Pus draining from a white line abscess.

5.7   Removal of under-run horn.

5.5   The internationally accepted code for the zones of the hoof.

Toe ulcer

Sole ulcer

Heel ulcer

In neglected cases the corium may be so badly damaged that the pedal bone itself becomes exposed (Illus. 5.8). Following the application of a block to the sound claw, this cow recovered well and remained in the herd for at least a further three lactations. Illus. 5.9 shows a white line infection which has tracked under the laminae of the wall to burst at the coronary band. Even in this case, all under-run horn has to be removed (Illus. 5.10).

There is a body of opinion that says it is better to leave a bridge of horn joining the two halves of the hoof wall to minimise movement and promote healing. I do not agree with this. Personally I think it is best to make quite sure that you have removed all of the under-run and infected horn, as only then can healing be complete. If a block is placed under the

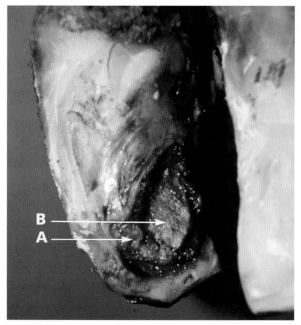

5.8 In neglected cases the corium (A) may be totally eroded to expose the pedal bone (B).

5.9 White line infection discharging at the coronary band.

5.10 Track opened and drained by removing the wall.

sound claw (described at the end of this chapter) to reduce weight bearing, the deep wall fissure seen in Illus. 5.10 is filled surprisingly quickly with 'cement' originating from the papillary and laminar corium.

Removing the Adjacent Wall

When draining a white line abscess, it is important that the small segment of wall adjacent to the infected track is opened up for drainage. If an attempt is made to drain infection by using only the curved tip of the hoof-knife, there is a danger that the hole will refill with dirt and debris and that lameness will recur. Removing a small segment of wall not only improves drainage considerably, but it also makes access to, and therefore removal of, further under-run sole or wall much easier. Illus. 5.11 and 5.12 demonstrate this effect, but on a normal hoof. The approach should be one of 'open-cast quarrying' and not 'deep-pit mining'!

The initial point of white line penetration may vary from a large, black area (Illus. 5.2) impacted with obviously visible dirt, stones or grit, to a minute focus, no larger than a pinhead. When some of these small tracks are followed down, there may be little more to see than a small change in the colouring of the horn.

As a general rule, if the track is black, it is going

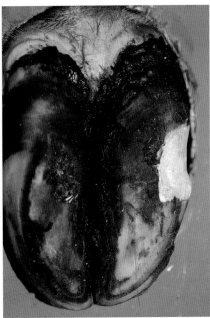

characteristically sited in the central solear area, towards the heel. They are often covered by a ledge of solear horn, which protrudes towards the interdigital space. A typical ledge is seen in Illus. 3.20. Sometimes the surface of the hoof appears normal; only when dishing the axial sole area during routine hoof trimming is the ulcer detected.

Some appear as a central haemorrhagic area (Illus. 5.13), which on further paring reveals an ulcer and under-run

5.11 Searching for white line pus: a crevice cut out by the tip of the hoof-knife is likely to become impacted.

5.12 White line pus: removing the side of the wall prevents impaction of debris.

from the outside inwards, and should be followed. If it is red, for example as in the right claw of Illus. 2.13, it is blood coming from the inside outwards, so it can be left alone. Large, homogeneous black areas (for example, as in the left claw in Illus. 2.13 and in the right claw of Illus. 5.6 and 5.7) should also be left, as these are the normal black pigmented areas of the hoof. The white wall at the toe in Illus. 2.13 contrasts sharply with the adjacent area of black sole, and shows very clearly how the two parts of the hoof originate from different structures.

The use of dressings and blocks (e.g. 'Cowslips') are discussed in the treatment section later in this chapter

Sole Ulcer

Table 5.1 highlights the importance of sole ulcers as one of the four conditions – the other three being white line disease, digital dermatitis and foul – which account for most of the lameness seen in the UK.

Sole ulcers typically occur on the lateral (outer) claw of the hind foot and, less commonly, on the medial (inner) claw of front feet and are

Lesion causing lameness	Cases per 100 cows per year
Sole ulcer	13.9
White line disease	12.7
Digital dermatitis	12.0
'Foul'	7.2
Heel ulcers	5.8
Foreign body penetration	3.1
Interdigital skin hyperplasia	1.2
Thin soles and bruising	2.0
Axial wall fissures	1.07
Deep pedal infection	0.45

Table 5.1. The major lesions causing lameness in a study of five UK dairy herds (54)

sole beneath (Illus. 5.14). In others, such as the heifer depicted in Illus. 5.15-5.17, the haemorrhage extends to the axial wall at the interdigital space. There is little to see superficially, but removal of a sliver of solear ledge reveals typical haemorrhage (Illus. 5.15) which initially increases in severity with increasing depth. However, comparison of Illus.

5.17 with Illus. 5.16 shows how the haemorrhage is arranged in layers down through the sole.

It has been possible to pare away some of the haemorrhage in 5.16, leaving normal horn beneath. The distance from the solear corium to the most superficial haemorrhage gives an indication of when the initial laminitic insult, producing the sole ulcer, first occurred, since horn grows at approximately 5 mm per month (see Chapter Two).

Sole ulcers are often slower to heal than the under-run sole lesions that result from white line abscesses or foreign body penetration. This is because an under-run sole is simply separation of the horn from the horn forming tissue, but the horn-producing tissues remain intact. A sole ulcer, on the other hand, is the result of damage to the

5.13 Haemorrhage at the sole ulcer site.

5.14 Ulcer and adjacent under-run sole.

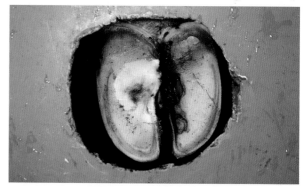

5.15 Haemorrhage in the sole of a heifer's foot.

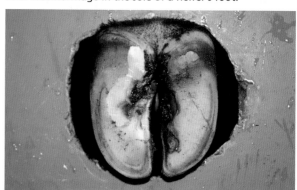

5.16 Exposure of the sole ulcer.

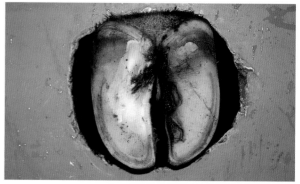

5.17 At this deeper level much of the haemorrhage in the sole has been pared away.

horn-forming tissue and the underlying corium itself. New horn is therefore much slower to form and a sole ulcer is much slower to heal.

Many ulcers never fully recover and cows may remain with a chronic low-grade lameness, needing corrective foot trimming two to four times a year for the rest of their productive lives. One trial *(56)* showed that cows that developed lameness in their first lactation were more much likely to become lame in subsequent lactations, and they suggested level of yield as a contributory factor.

Treatment

The treatment of sole ulcers consists of four main steps:

1. Dish the sole as much as possible, so that weight is no longer taken on the ulcer area. This was done for the heifer in Illus. 5.15 to 5.17.

2. Where possible, pare back the affected claw to its minimum size, but leave the sound claw large and weight-bearing, thus taking further weight off the ulcer.

3. Remove infected and under-run horn from around the edge of the ulcer, i.e. remove the horn being lifted by the hoof-knife in Illus. 5.14.

4. Often lumps of granulation tissue (proud flesh) protrude from the ulcer site, as in Illus. 5.18. These should be removed so that the corium is flush with the sole (Illus. 5.19), thus allowing new horn to grow over the initial lesion. Removal can be by amputation or by application of an astringent dressing.

The value of a copper sulphate dressing or other astringents, or even a calf disbudding iron to burn out granulation tissue within the ulcer, is debatable *(15)*. While it might destroy the granulation tissue, I feel that it also damages the developing new horn (i.e. the corium and its covering of epidermis) and therefore any long-term application is contra-indicated.

A bulky bandage retaining the dressing could also transfer weight onto the ulcer site, and thus

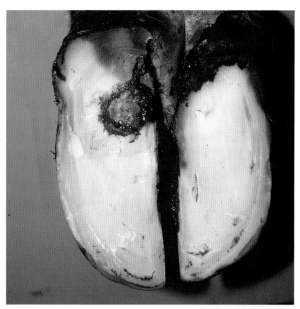

5.18 Proud flesh protruding from the ulcer.

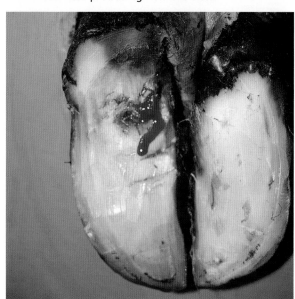

5.19 Proud flesh amputated.

increase the bruising of the area. Furthermore, by retaining any infection the dressing might retard healing. However, others consider that a dressing is worthwhile. As ulcers are slow to heal, applying a block to the sound claw to remove weight bearing from the ulcer is an excellent measure to promote recovery. One survey showed that if first-lactation animals made a full recovery from their ulcers at the first treatment their future prospects were good. However, if the first ulcer did not heal, they were likely to be affected with ulcers for the rest of their lives. It is therefore important to treat early and well. Further details of dressing and blocks are given in the Individual Treatments section later in this chapter

Ulcers are situated on the sole of the foot, just beneath the posterior tip of the pedal bone, at the point of attachment of the deep flexor tendon (Illus. 2.30 and 5.20). In Illus. 5.20 note how the horn of the sole has become indented by the rear edge of the pedal bone at 'A', and how loss of the heel at 'B' further destabilises the foot.

An ulcer develops from a disruption of the

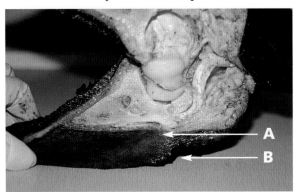

5.20 Extensive heel necrosis (B) has removed support from beneath the rear edge of the pedal bone, leading to sole indentation (A) and the start of the formation of an ulcer.

corium. The disrupted corium produces defective hoof which eventually is seen as a sole ulcer. The corium also feeds the bone, however, so inflammation of the corium can also lead to adverse changes in the bone. Illus. 5.21 compares a normal pedal bone (right) with a boiled-out specimen from a cow with a chronic and long-standing sole ulcer (left). Note how the base and edges of the affected bone are roughened with exostoses (bony overgrowths), especially around the joint. This will lead to pain and discomfort when walking. As the exostoses will persist even when the ulcer has healed, early detection and

prompt, effective treatment are important if such permanent damage is to be avoided.

Penetrating infection from a deep ulcer could lead

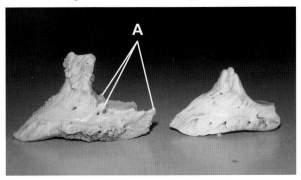

5.21 A long-standing sole ulcer leads to irreversible changes in the pedal bone. A normal bone is shown on the right. Note the exostoses (A) on the left pedal bone.

to abscess formation in the digital cushion, the navicular bursa, navicular bone or even the pedal joint itself. Abscesses in the bursa are sometimes referred to as 'retro-articular' abscesses, meaning literally 'behind the joint'. When these deeper infections are involved, there will be more severe lameness with swelling of the skin above the coronary band; application of pressure to the heel may produce a purulent discharge from the original ulcer site. Pus can be seen discharging from an ulcer in Illus. 5.22. A wooden

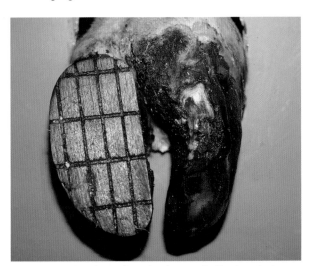

5.22 Pus oozing from the sole ulcer, an indication that deeper structures are involved and that more radical treatment is needed.

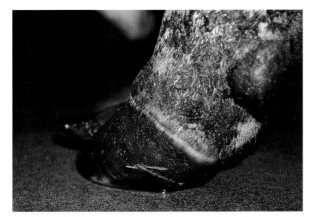

5.23 Dorsal (Upward) rotation of the toe following rupture of the deep flexor tendon.

block has been applied to the sound claw. Veterinary attention will be needed to produce drainage of infection from these deeper tissues, and the options are deep pedal fenestration, a drainage tube, or amputation. These techniques are discussed in more detail in the section on 'deeper infections' later in this chapter (p. 64). If the ulcer is deep, total rupture of the deep flexor tendon may occur, leaving the cow with a permanently turned-up toe, as seen in Illus. 5.23.

Heel and Toe Ulcers

Although sole ulcers are by far the most common, there can be areas of haemorrhage or even total perforation at other areas of the sole. Sole ulcers typically occur in an axial position on the *axial* aspect in the centre of zone 4 (Illus. 5.5) *(51a)*. Toe ulcers are seen in zone 5 at the toe, and heel ulcers are in the *central* sole region at the junction of zones 4 and 6.

Toe Ulcers

Toe ulcers are thought to occur when the pedal bone sinks within the hoof 'bows first'. That is, the front of the pedal bone drops before the flexor tuberosity at the rear. A typical example was shown in Illus. 2.26. Toe ulcers also occur in bulls that have been introduced to walk on a concrete yard system without sufficient acclimatisation, or not given sufficient rest. They seem to bruise the toes of their front feet when dismounting from serving. Soft soles

in over-worked bulls are discussed later in this section.

Toe ulcers may be seen in young beef cattle a few weeks after they have been introduced into a large beef yard or feedlot system, especially if they have first been transported for long distances. In this instance it seems that they spend so long standing, and perhaps reversing away from threatening situations, that they wear through their toes. Toe ulcers are also seen in grazing situations, where inadequately acclimatised animals are expected to walk long distances after calving.

Heel Ulcers

Heel ulcers are recognised as small dark red/black marks (Illus. 5.24) in the central sole area towards the heel *(23)*. Illus. 5.24 shows a typical heel ulcer on the left claw and haemorrhage at the site of an early sole ulcer on the right claw. Some heel ulcers simply track down to the corium and fade to nothing. Others lead to under-running and a large abscess in the sole at the sole – heel junction (Illus. 5.25) which can produce marked lameness. Heel ulcers represent a significant cause of lameness (Table 5.1).

They often occur in association with sole ulcers, although they are seen more commonly on the medial claw of hind feet than sole ulcers, which are seen primarily on the lateral claw. The cause of heel ulcers is not known, although one theory is that they are produced by the pinching of the corium under the caudal edge of the pedal bone. At this point the bone is suspended in the pedal suspensory apparatus, within which there are three fat pads

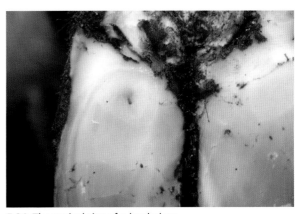

5.24 The typical site of a heel ulcer.

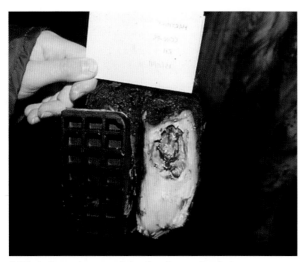

5.25 A deep abscess originating from a heel ulcer.

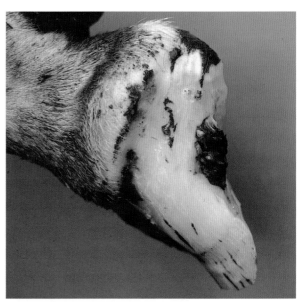

5.26 Protrusion of granulation tissue.

acting as shock absorbers, as described in Illus. 2.21 *(79)*. If the fat pads start to degenerate (Illus. 2.22), the central fat pad has been shown to undergo cartilaginous change. It has been proposed that it is the effect of this 'pea' of cartilage that leads to the formation of heel ulcers, just as if you were standing with a stone in your shoe.

Deeper Pedal Infections

In a proportion of cases of white line disease or sole ulcers lameness appears to improve following drainage of pus, but then recurs five to seven days later. Re-examination of the foot may reveal a dark black-red, fleshy lump of granulation tissue (proud flesh) pushing through the wound, as in Illus. 5.26. There may also be swelling and/or reddening of the hairless coronary area, as in Illus. 5.26, and as the swelling increases, the lameness becomes increasingly severe. This is usually an indication that further under-run horn exists, or that there is a deeper infection present and it is certainly an indication for the administration of antibiotics by injection. If the lesion was just a simple under-run sole from a sole ulcer or white line defect, then antibiotic injection is unlikely to be either necessary or cost effective, especially as it may require milk to be withheld.

In this case, the wall was under-run to the coronary band. Removal of the wall (Illus. 5.27) and application of a block to the sound claw effected a fairly rapid recovery (granulation tissue has no nerve supply and hence its removal causes little pain), but as the affected claw was swollen, additional antibiotic treatment was necessary.

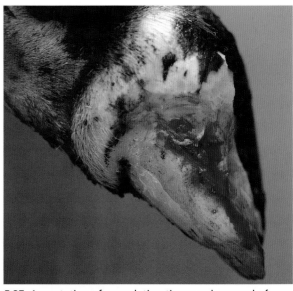

5.27 Amputation of granulation tissue and removal of further under-run wall.

5.27 Amputation of granulation tissue

In advanced or neglected cases, the affected claw starts to swell and may discharge at the coronary band (Illus. 5.28). The cow will be acutely lame. This is an indication that infection has penetrated deeper structures, for example the navicular bursa, the navicular bone, flexor tendon sheath or even the pedal joint itself. (These structures are shown in Illus. 2.7, 2.23 and 3.7.) Veterinary attention should be sought rapidly for such cases, as they will require drainage of the deep tissues and aggressive antibiotic therapy. The three main techniques for dealing with such infections are:

- deep pedal fenestration
- insertion of a drainage tube
- claw amputation.

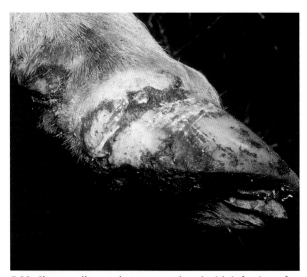

5.28 Claw swollen at the coronary band with infection of deeper tissues. Radical treatment is required. *(D. Weaver)*

All three are deeply invasive procedures and should not be attempted without anaesthesia or suitable training. **Deep pedal fenestration**, or 'coring', consists of making a large opening on the wall or sole to drain the deep infection. It is best performed by squeezing the infected foot to locate the position of natural discharge of infection. This is often seen as a small bead of pus appearing on the surface of the foot, as shown in Illus. 5.29. Even though a PVC shoe ('Cowslip') has been applied to the sound claw, the cow remains very lame due to pressure of infection deep within the foot. The pus and infection must be drained to affect a cure. If the point of the hoof-knife is carefully inserted along the pus track to the depth of the abscess, and then a large hole is made from

5.29 A small bead of pus appearing at the sole ulcer site indicates deep infection.

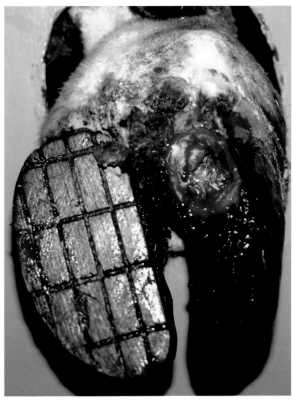

5.30 Under anaesthesia a large drainage hole is created from the depth of the abscess.

5.31 A tube inserted using a trocar and cannula allows the deep pedal abscess to be flushed from the inside.

the abscess to the surface of the foot (Illus. 5.30), many such abscesses drain quite well. The hole must be flushed regularly to ensure good drainage.

Full veterinary anaesthesia is likely to be necessary to perform this procedure, but despite the size of the drainage hole, resolution can be surprisingly rapid. Healing is improved by regular flushing of the cavity with water, or simply hosing the foot with water when the cow is in the milking parlour, as this prevents the drainage hole from sealing over. Aggressive antibiotic cover for five to eight days is essential, and pain relief, e.g. flunixin or meloxicam daily, will be necessary.

The second technique involves using a **trocar and cannula** to insert a tube in through the site of pus discharge and out above the coronary band, as shown in Illus. 5.31. The lower end of the tube is tied off in a knot, and water infused into the top of the tube attached to the hock discharges out

through holes in the tube inside the wound. This technique is more invasive and takes a little longer to implement but has the advantage that the wound is being flushed internally. Again, anaesthesia is required, followed by post-operative aggressive antibiotic cover and pain relief.

The third option, **amputation of a diseased claw**, works well provided the case is selected carefully. Details of the technique are outside the scope of this book, and the following points are made for the interest of those readers who are already familiar with the basics of the technique.

Amputation should only be attempted if the *sound* claw has a good depth of heel, a good angle to the anterior wall and is not swollen due to infection spreading from the diseased claw. Regional intravenous anaesthesia is ideal, although good anaesthesia can often be obtained simply by injecting 25–30 ml of procaine or lignocaine into the interdigital space. A tourniquet is essential. Use a scalpel to incise at least 20 mm dorsally into the interdigital cleft, so that the wire cut is high. Compared to the other techniques there is an additional requirement to regularly re-dress the lesion, and the extra weight bearing on the remaining digit may lead to early culling.

A single dressing change after two or a

maximum of three days is ideal, with the second dressing fully removed two to three days later. Do not leave the dressing on for too long, as this can seriously retard healing. Most cases heal remarkably well. I have amputated claws in front feet, including the front foot of a bull, and many cases have lasted for several lactations.

Foreign Body Penetration of the Sole

Although penetration of the white line is by far the most common site of penetration in the foot (because it is a point of weakness), any part of the sole can be damaged by a sharp object.

Typical foreign bodies are sharp stones, pieces of glass or tin, nails (especially those used for securing felt, which are short with a large flat head), and I have even seen the sharp roots of cast teeth penetrating the sole!

Sometimes, when a lame cow is examined, the foreign body is still present, but often it is missing and all that remains is a black track, distinguishable from a white line penetration lesion only by its position, i.e. it is not on the white line (Illus. 5.32).

It is not sufficient simply to remove the nail (or other foreign body) from the sole, since it will have carried infection in with it and the original point of entry will not be large enough to provide sufficient drainage. The hole should be opened and all under-run sole and adjacent wall removed (Illus. 5.33). As with white line penetration, the lesion consists of separation of horn from the horn-forming tissue, so that when the under-run sole has been removed, new horn is exposed. The application of a dressing is again optional. Most cases heal better without one. If at all possible, the affected claw (the right one in Illus. 5.33) should be trimmed so that it is smaller than the sound claw.

Alternatively, apply a block to the sound claw to minimise weight bearing, improve recovery rates and reduce pain. In this example there also appears to be further under-run horn that should be removed.

Illus. 5.34 shows a stone impacted into the sole of a bull's foot. The cavity left in the sole after the stone has been removed (Illus. 5.35) needs to be opened up by further paring, otherwise more debris might become impacted.

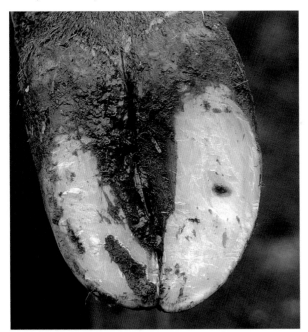

5.32 Foreign body (nail) penetration of the sole.

5.33 Removal of under-run sole following nail penetration.

5.34 A stone impacted into the sole of a bull's foot.

5.35 The cavity left by the stone. This must be pared away.

Vertical Fissure or Sandcrack

Sandcracks occur as a result of damage to the periople, the area of soft horn which originates at the skin – hoof junction at the coronary band. The periople gives a thin, shiny, wax-like coating to the hoof and covers the heel. Sandcracks are seen in older cows in hot, dry, sandy conditions and may also be a consequence of digital dermatitis involving the coronary band. The damaged coronary area fails to produce intact horn and as the adjacent hoof continues to grow, the defect appears as a fissure in the wall. A two-year Canadian field study of 265 Hereford beef cows with a 37 per cent prevalence of sandcracks demonstrated that supplementation with 10 mg/day of biotin significantly reduced the incidence of sandcracks from 29.4 per cent to 14.3 per cent (26).

Illus. 5.36 shows a sandcrack in both claws, one extending almost to the toe. If it is shallow (i.e. the corium is not involved), no lameness results. However, because there is very little space between the hoof and the pedal bone at the front of the foot (Illus. 2.3), when infection occurs, just a minute quantity of pus is sufficient to cause severe lameness. Opening the track and draining the pus, using the curved tip of the hoof-knife, produces rapid relief.

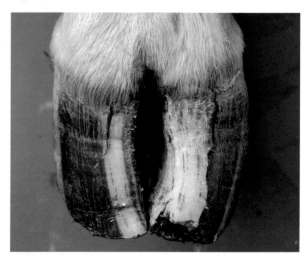

5.36 A vertical fissure (sandcrack).

If movement occurs between the two sides of the fissure, granulation tissue (proud flesh) may develop (Illus. 5.37). This is best treated by removing the granulation tissue, opening the track slightly and, in severe cases, applying a wooden or rubber block to the sound claw, so that further movement within the fissure is limited.

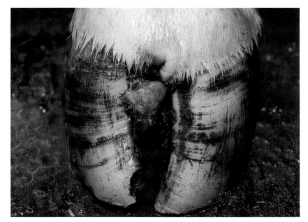

5.37 Proud flesh protruding from a vertical fissure.

Horizontal Fissure

Horizontal cracks can also occur (Illus. 5.38) and often go unnoticed until they have grown down towards the toe. Any severe illness, for example mastitis, metritis or toxaemia, e.g. from the over-eating of concentrates, can lead to a total, but temporary, cessation of horn production. When horn formation starts again, movement of hoof continues down over the laminae, but there may be a complete

circumferential fissure around the wall of the hoof, relating to the interruption of horn formation.

The cow in Illus. 5.38 is a good example of lameness due to horizontal fissures. She had recovered (just!) from an acute *E. coli* mastitis some five to six months previously. She was running with the dry cows and starting to put on weight when she developed lameness in all four feet.

As the 'thimble' of old horn passes down towards the toe, it loses its attachment at the heel and there is an increased opportunity for movement between the old and new horn. Small stones and other debris can then penetrate the crevice and produce infection. Both movement and infection cause pain and lameness, although a significant number of thimbles simply break off and are shed from the toe, without causing any particular problem. The cow in Illus. 5.39 was not lame. She was about to shed the toe thimble on the right as it is obviously loose. This is sometimes referred to as a 'broken toe'.

When lameness occurs, the thimble of loose horn should be removed with a hoof-knife and clippers (not an easy task) and, ideally, a block applied to the sound claw. Sometimes (as in Illus. 5.38) all eight claws in all four feet are affected and the cow is probably best culled.

Less severe attacks of laminitis are seen as grooves, circling the front of the hoof as in Illus. 5.40. These have been referred to as hardship lines (50). The date when they were formed (and therefore possibly their cause) can be determined

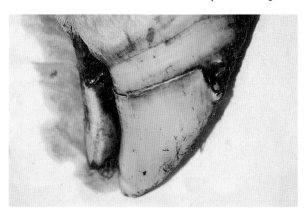

5.38 A horizontal fissure.

5.39 A horizontal fissure shedding naturally ('broken toe').

by measuring the distance from the hardship line to the coronary band. Hoof grows at approximately 5 mm per month.

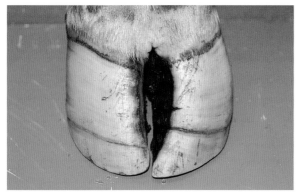

5.40 Hardship lines.

Axial Wall Fissures

In Chapter Two we saw how the white line junction runs along the abaxial (outer) wall from the heel to the toe, then back along the axial wall at sole level, before passing obliquely up the axial wall to the coronary band in the interdigital space. White line lesions running obliquely along the axial wall are often referred to as axial wall fissures (Illus. 5.41), although fissures may also be present parallel with, but not involving the white line. Recently there has been an apparent increase in incidence (99), especially in the lateral hind claws. The cause is unknown, but suggestions include excess standing and wet conditions underfoot. Cows with corkscrew

and other claw rotation problems may show an increased incidence; digital dermatitis lesions affecting the coronary band in the interdigital space may be a further factor. Digital dermatitis can only be a contributory cause, however, because in New Zealand axial wall fissures are common, but dermatitis is rare. Due to their position in the interdigital space they are quite difficult to pare and lesions which damage the coronary band can lead to permanent axial wall fissures, similar to Illus. 5.37.

Thin Sole Syndrome

It is not uncommon to lift the foot of a heifer - or of a young bull running with a dairy herd - and find that the sole can be compressed by finger pressure, and this produces pain. The syndrome occurs under environmental circumstances where the rate of wear, and especially wear of the wall, exceeds the rate of growth. It can also arise from over-trimming, especially if power tools are being used. It is becoming a serious issue in total confinement systems, especially where feet are often moist, e.g. in North America (97). Illus. 5.42 shows the foot of a young bull over-worked in a dairy herd. Note how the wall of the hoof has been worn away and that weight is now taken by the sole, leading to haemorrhage and sole fissures. In early-lactation heifers the syndrome is normally associated with excess standing, and the factors involved are discussed in Chapter Six. The only

5.41 Axial wall fissure running along the axial wall.

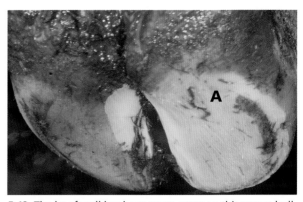

5.42 The hoof wall has been worn away on this young bull, leading to excess wear on the sole. Note also the sole fissure at A.

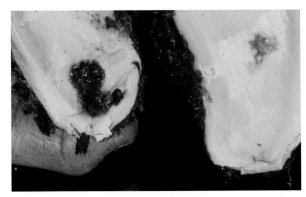

5.43 Toe necrosis showing the typical foul-smelling track at the toe.

examination there will probably be a characteristic foul odour and even with further extensive removal of under-run tissues often the toe fails to heal (Illus. 5.43).

In such cases it is probable that the apex of the pedal bone has become infected (i.e. osteomyelitis of the pedal bone). Illus. 5.44 shows an eroded pedal bone from a case of pedal necrosis compared with a normal bone on the right. Note how the inflamed corium has left the eroded bone with a very pitted and irregular surface compared to the normal. This irregular surface can also lead to pain.

Causes of apical necrosis include excess wear at the toe leading to soft soles, and white line lesions on the axial wall. The incidence seems to be higher in herds where digital dermatitis is poorly controlled, so possibly secondary dermatitis, reducing the rate of healing of the corium, is also a factor. A similar condition is seen in weaned suckler calves that continually run around the pen when introduced into feed lots.

Treatment must involve removal of all under-run horn and necrotic bone. Some clinicians report good success with such aggressive debraiding. Provided the coronary band remains intact, removal of the necrotic toe and the adjacent wall and sole (anaesthesia required) with an embryotomy wire may result in full resolution. Ideally an X-ray is needed to identify the extent of the necrosis and, as many pedal bones are already severely eroded (Illus. 5.44), total amputation of the digit may be the best option. Because only the toe is involved, these cases respond well to amputation.

useful treatment is rest. For instance, take the heifers or young bulls out of the cubicle system and house them on a straw yard where they have ample opportunity to lie down. The period of rest may have to be for one to two months, because if the sole is easily compressed it is likely to be only 2–3 mm thick, so with growth at 5 mm per month, it will take at the very least a month for the damage to repair.

Bulls running with a dairy herd should be given regular periods of rest. For instance, they can be placed in a straw yard at night after running with the cows during the day. Another means is to use a second bull so that they work alternate days. Large bulls commonly do not find cubicles comfortable, so they spend longer standing, leading to increased hoof wear. Young bulls, especially, will also often follow cows around in the pro-oestrous phase, i.e. for the twenty-four hours before the cow comes on heat, and this further increases hoof wear. Toe ulcers are often associated with a similar syndrome, and this is discussed in an earlier section.

BONE CONDITIONS

Apical Necrosis of the Pedal Bone

In a few cows, what initially appears to be a standard white line abscess at the toe sometimes fails to heal, even though it may appear to have been treated adequately. Lameness is moderate only, but because the cow walks on her heel to protect her toe, the toe becomes considerably overgrown. At the second

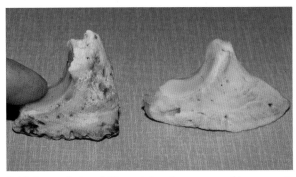

5.44 An eroded pedal bone taken from a case of toe necrosis.

Fracture of the Pedal Bone

Any severe trauma to the sole of the foot could, in theory, cause a fracture of the pedal bone. The fracture line usually runs from the centre of the pedal joint to the base of the bone (Illus. 5.45). Many older cows have a groove running across the articular (joint) surface of the pedal bone, which has been suggested as a predisposing factor to fracture at this site. Oestrus behaviour, with the mounting cow falling heavily onto a rough surface, is one cause. Bones weakened by age, fluorine poisoning or a penetrating infection from the hoof may also fracture.

5.46 The cross-legged stance of a cow suffering from fracture of the pedal bone.

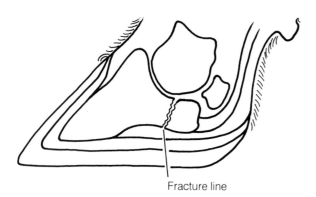

Fracture line

5.45 Fracture of the pedal bone. The fracture line commonly runs from the centre of the pedal joint to the base of the pedal bone.

Typically the medial (inner) claw of the front foot is involved and by adopting a cross-legged stance as in Illus. 5.46, weight is transferred onto the sound (lateral) claw. However, the stance alone is not sufficient to indicate a fractured pedal bone. Cows with ulcers in both medial claws will adopt a similar stance.

Affected animals often show little or no heat or swelling of the foot, although there may be pain when the hoof is pinched. Veterinary attention should be sought. The hoof acts as an excellent splint for the pedal bone and, provided that a block is applied to the sound claw, many cases heal within two to three months.

INDIVIDUAL TREATMENTS

Use of Dressings

Opinions vary on the need to apply a dressing following removal of an under-run sole, or on a sole ulcer. An increasing number of people (including the author) consider that a dressing produces little additional benefit and, if the dressing is left on for longer than one to two days it can be counter-productive.

There is no significant risk of infection from the environment (i.e. slurry) penetrating the layer of epithelium covering the corium and, if left exposed, new horn forms very quickly. The application of a dressing, especially if it is bulky, has several disadvantages, for example:

- Dressings may prevent drainage of infection.

- Their bulk could increase the pressure and weight bearing on the corium and thus retard healing

- If left too long they can cut into the coronary band.

- A dressing may lead to the wound 'sweating'. Wounds do not heal well in the absence of air.

The use of a dressing to hold topical antibiotic in place in the treatment of digital dermatitis is well worth while, although even here it should only be left in place for three to four days maximum. A dressing is also needed to control haemorrhage after surgery, such as digit amputation, and, in severe cases, can be used in combination with a block.

At one time I almost always applied a bandage. I rarely do so now. It is, however, of benefit to ensure that the wound is washed clean regularly, e.g. by spraying the foot with water when the cow comes in for milking, or by walking her daily through a disinfectant foot bath.

Use of Blocks

Resting the affected claw is highly beneficial, promoting healing and improving cow comfort and welfare. This is frequently attempted by hoof paring, i.e. by leaving the sound claw higher and therefore with greater weight bearing. The most commonly used appliances are plastic shoes glued to the wall and sole, wooden or rubber blocks glued to the sole and nail-on rubber blocks. Fixing

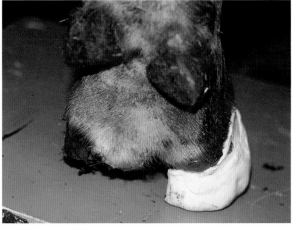

5.47 The glue fully covers the block. The affected claw is well off the ground.

a wooden block (Illus. 5.47) or PVC shoe (e.g. 'Cowslip', Illus. 5.48) onto the sole of the sound claw, thus lifting the affected claw off the ground, is an excellent treatment and rapidly facilitates healing. White line lesions in the axial wall (site 4 on Illus. 5.1) are particularly painful and are strong candidates for such treatment.

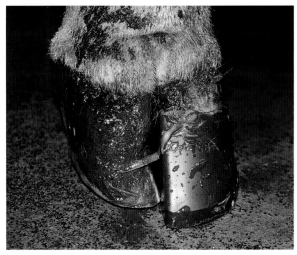

5.48 A glue-on plastic shoe (47).

Wooden blocks

Preparation of the hoof, either by thoroughly scraping it with a hoof-knife (Illus. 5.49) or by using an electric sander, is the most important part of fixing a wooden block or a PVC shoe. Before the glue is applied, all parts of the hoof should be clean and dry. Even touching the cleaned surfaces with your fingers may produce a greasy surface and reduce adhesion. If the affected claw has a bleeding area it can be difficult to prevent blood splashing onto the claw to be blocked, although attaching a long, plastic rectal examination sleeve produces a 'drain' for the blood and helps considerably. Forcing the claws apart with a 3 to 5 cm length of 7.5 mm thick dowelling or a rolled-up wad of paper, improves access to the axial walls and makes cleaning and gluing easier (Illus. 5.50). Mix the glue to a fairly stiff consistency, then apply a layer to the sole, to the sides of the hoof and to the surface of the block to be fixed.

5.49 Clean the hoof before applying the glue for a Demotec wooden block *(41)*.

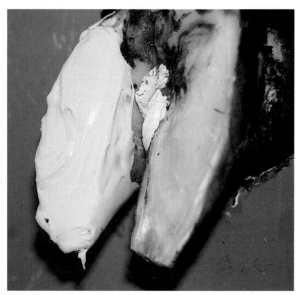

5.50 Apply the glue to the sole and walls. Note the wad of paper forcing the claws apart, thus improving access to the axial wall.

Next, push the block firmly onto the sole. Excess glue will be squeezed out; draw this over the sides of the block to improve adhesion. Any remaining glue can be applied to the heel or, if there is sufficient, to cover the whole block, thereby improving adhesion, strength and weight-bearing.

The front tip of the block should be kept at least level with, and perhaps slightly back from, the toe and preferably slightly overlapping the heel, as in Illus. 5.47. A block placed too far forward (Illus. 5.51) makes the cow walk back on her heels, producing considerable discomfort and uneven and rapid wear of the block.

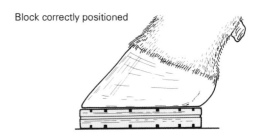

Block correctly positioned

5.51 The wooden block below is applied too far forward of the toe. This is uncomfortable, making the cow walk back on her heels.

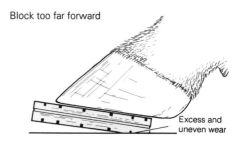

Block too far forward

Excess and uneven wear

It is also an advantage not to have the block overlapping the sole at the sides. Many commercially available blocks seem too large and I regularly cut off a sliver (Illus. 5.52) to make them smaller. This uses less glue and improves adhesion.

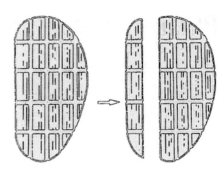

5.52 Many commercial blocks are too wide. Removal of a sliver improves adhesion.

Quick-setting adhesives are now available, allowing the wooden block to adhere within a few minutes, even in the winter.

PVC Shoes

Personally I use mainly PVC shoes *(47)* (Illus. 5.48). They are applied following a similar thorough cleaning of the foot . They have advantages over wooden blocks in that a) the glue is mixed in the shoe, b) the PVC heel is slower to wear away than a wooden block, c) the side wall of the shoe supports the hoof, and d) most importantly, the glue sets more quickly than conventional adhesives, even in cold weather, and especially if the bottle of solvent is kept warm, e.g. by storing it in your pocket before use.

When the glue is first mixed it is quite fluid in nature. Wait until the setting process starts and the glue mix becomes thick enough such that it will not run out of the shoe when the shoe is tilted. Smear the glue all over the inner surface of the shoe to achieve good cover, then push the shoe hard onto the foot. Keep the wall of the shoe in close contact with the wall of the hoof, and do not be concerned that a gap is present at the heel. Any surplus glue that is squeezed out from between the hoof wall and the shoe can be placed into the gap between the sole of the shoe and the foot at the heel. This helps to lift the heel and maintain the correct angle of the hoof.

As with wooden blocks, it is essential that the Cowslip shoe is pushed far enough back to support the heel. With Cowslips this may entail some trimming of the sound claw prior to application. If correctly applied, both PVC shoes and wooden blocks should stay on for at least two months, during which time it is remarkable how quite severe lesions will heal. However, if the heel is becoming worn, then the PVC shoe or block should be removed, because walking will be uncomfortable. One study *(21)* found that Cowslips stayed on for an average of seventy-four days, enough time for the sole to grow to approximately 12 mm, whereas a study in Uruguay *(81)* found that wooden blocks stayed on for an average of forty-two days.

Nail-on rubber blocks

Rubber blocks can be nailed on (Illus. 5.53). They are cheaper and easier to apply, but not universally popular because of the danger of nails penetrating the corium, leading to infection. Moreover, they do not stay on as long as glued blocks and, when they fall off, there is a risk of solar penetration by the shed nails.

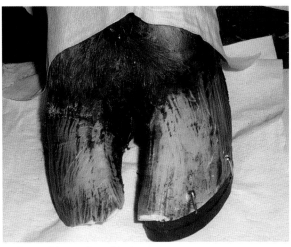

5.53 A rubber nail-on block.

Illus. 5.54 shows the importance of the positioning of the nails. 'A' will pass through the white line and with its bevelled edge deflecting it outwards will pass out through the wall, totally avoiding all sensitive tissues. However, 'B' is well inside the white line and although it will still reappear on the side of the wall to be clinched over, it has penetrated the corium en route and this will lead to infection, pain and lameness.

Before you apply a nail-on block it is essential that you ensure that the sole has been trimmed to provide a sound and level weight-bearing surface, and that there are no lesions present which could in themselves produce lameness. Hold the foot firmly and hammer the nails, bevelled edge innermost, through the white line area of the sole. With its one-sided bevel, the nail will curve

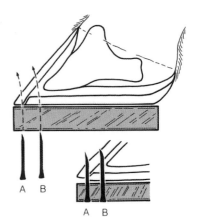

5.54 The correct positioning of the nails for a rubber block. A nail inserted into the white line at 'A' will pass out through the hoof wall without damaging sensitive tissues. 'B' is passing inside the white line and will penetrate the corium, leading to infection, pain and lameness.

outwards slightly, to reappear through the wall where it can be clinched over. Lubrication of the nails assists their penetration. It is often easiest to insert the first nail towards the toe, to establish the position of the block and the second towards the heel. The remaining nail holes should then be in the correct position.

Plastic protective shoes

Plastic protective shoes (Illus. 5.55) were once popular. They were secured by tying them tightly at the fetlock, encasing both hooves. A dressing could be applied to the affected claw. Shoes were available with a block on the left or right side, thus lifting the affected claw and reducing its weight bearing.

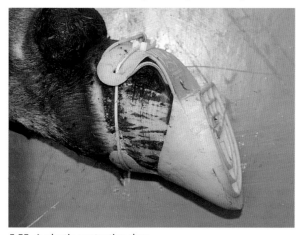

5.55 A plastic protective shoe.

However, they are less popular now, partly because they are difficult to secure and partly because the foot tends to become damp and sweaty inside the shoe, thus retarding healing.

Topical hoof products

A variety of topical products, hoof sprays, etc. are available on the market that claim to improve hoof health and decrease lameness. I have little personal experience of these, but as we know from Chapter Two that hoof grows from the corium and that it is disruption of the corium that produces defective hoof, it is difficult to understand how products applied to the outer surface of the hoof can have a major effect on hoof quality. Foot baths work because their effect is on the skin, not because of their effects on the hoof.

DISEASES OF THE DIGITAL SKIN

In the first sections of this chapter the main disorders of the hoof and bones were described. In this next section, disorders of the skin are discussed. The first of these, interdigital skin hyperplasia, is caused by chronic irritation. The other three – digital dermatitis, 'foul' ('foot rot') and mud fever – are caused by different *infectious* disorders; because of this, foot hygiene is very important in their control.

Interdigital Corns or Growths
(Interdigital Skin Hyperplasia)

These are also called corns, interdigital granulomas, tylomas or fibromas, but the correct name is interdigital skin hyperplasia, since the lump is simply an overgrowth of normal skin. A typical example is seen in Illus. 5.56. In every cow there is a small fold of skin adjacent to the axial (inner) wall of each claw in the interdigital space and hence hyperplasia (skin over-growth) can develop from either side. The growths are caused by chronic irritation to the underlying skin. The major causes of the skin inflammation are thought to be:

- Chronic digital dermatitis.
- Low-grade 'foul'.
- Walking over very rough surfaces such as bricks in gateways, very poor pitted concrete or frosted fields, all of which lead to excessive splaying of the claws.
- Removal of the axial (inner) wall during hoof trimming. This leads to the claws splaying outwards (Illus. 4.22) away from each other, and stretches the interdigital skin.
- The condition may be inherited, being seen particularly in heavy breeds of dairy cows and in certain beef bulls such as Herefords.

An inflamed area of digital dermatitis is often found on the top of the skin hyperplasia lesion

(Illus. 5.57), and when digital dermatitis is brought under control in a herd, the incidence of these 'growths' commonly decreases. Secondary infection may occur, producing foul (Illus. 5.58), and of course any overlying digital dermatitis must be treated.

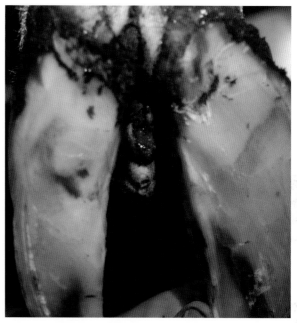

5.57 Interdigital skin hyperplasia with secondary digital dermatitis.

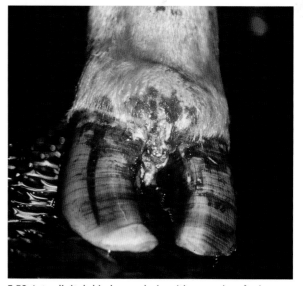

5.58 Interdigital skin hyperplasia with secondary foul.

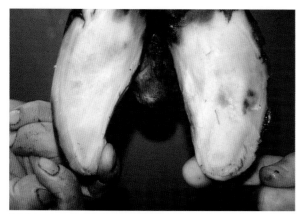

5.56 Interdigital skin hyperplasia.

Lameness is due to either the superficial digital dermatitis or to the claws compressing and pinching the swelling during walking. Hence removing horn from between the claws, thereby increasing the space within the interdigital cleft and preventing compression, is sufficient treatment for small skin growths. If it is no longer being pinched between the claws, the skin hyperplasia slowly disappears. Larger lesions require veterinary amputation, as shown in Illus. 5.59. Provided that only the superficial skin (the epidermis) is removed, there is little chance of excess bleeding or secondary infection. The risks increase if the underlying dermis is penetrated and fat deposits are exposed.

Regular foot-bathing, described for the control of digital dermatitis, is the most important control measure. If formalin is used daily, most growths disappear. Cows with persistent growths can be stood with their hind feet in a 6 mm depth 5 per cent formalin foot bath for ten to fifteen minutes each day, and this will decrease the size of the growths very well.

Foul in the Foot

This is also known (especially in North America) as 'foot rot' and there are a variety of colloquial names in the UK such as 'lewer' and 'claw ill'. The correct name for the condition is interdigital necrobacillosis. It is caused by an infection with the bacterium *Fusobacterium necrophorum*, possibly in association with a second bacterium, *Bacteroides melaninogenicus*. Both organisms are found in the faeces of normal cows. Cultural studies have suggested that *B. melaninogenicus* should be further divided into *Porphyromonas asaccharolytica* and *Prevotella* species. Damage to the interdigital skin, either by stones, sticks or these spirochaete bacteria, is thought to be needed before *Fusobacterium* can penetrate the underlying tissues.

Initially seen as a swelling of the coronary band (e.g. in the heifer in Illus. 5.60), which forces the two claws slightly apart, the characteristic feature of foul is a split in the interdigital skin, often discharging pus and lumps of degenerating tissue debris, as in Illus. 5.61. Some say that there is a characteristic smell. Personally I am not convinced about this.

The important feature in diagnosis is that the interdigital skin is split to expose the underlying and necrotic dermis. Whereas digital dermatitis is an

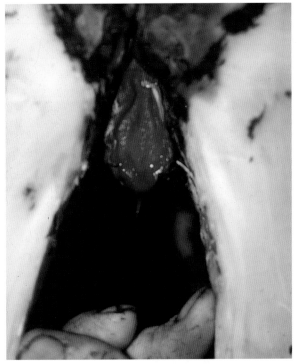

5.59 Large interdigital skin hyperplasia lesions require amputation.

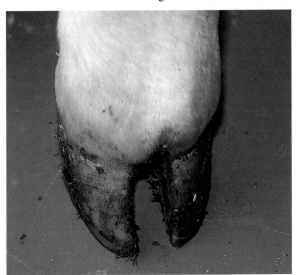

5.60 A heifer with foul. Note the swelling of the coronary band and the claws forced apart.

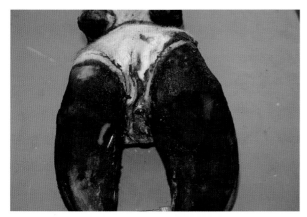

5.61 Foul, showing the typical split in the interdigital skin exposing the underlying dermis.

infection of the superficial layers of the skin (the epidermis), the characteristic of 'foul' is that it produces a toxin that causes necrosis and tissue degeneration in the deeper dermis. There are three strains of *F. necrophorum* and one is especially virulent. This is one reason why some cases of 'foul' are mild and others are much more severe.

In untreated cases the swelling may track up the tendon sheaths of the leg towards the fetlock and beyond, or may penetrate into the pedal joint itself. The latter produces an extremely severe and protracted lameness, often requiring amputation. In Illus. 5.61 the deep interdigital necrosis caused by foul appears to be producing some swelling of the right claw and must be extremely close to the pedal joint at this point.

Treatment, which should be administered promptly in order to avoid infection penetrating the joint, is normally by antibiotic injection, sometimes combined with anti-inflammatory and pain relief in more severe cases. At the same time the foot should always be lifted to ensure that there is not a stick or stone between the claws contributing to the foul.

Regular, i.e. daily, disinfectant foot baths (pages 86 – 120) are very effective in the control of herd outbreaks. If a high incidence of infection occurs, check that the feet are not being damaged by agents such as stones in muddy and poorly maintained gateways. Outbreaks of foul can also occur in young-stock, both housed and at pasture, and individual

cases may be seen in calves as young as two to three weeks. As with mastitis, an untreated individual case can act as a reservoir of infection for other cows, and hence the affected animal should be treated promptly and effectively, including topical spray if the interdidgital skin is split.

Superfoul

This is a peracute form of interdigital necrobacillosis with a poor response to treatment unless aggressive therapy is instigated in the very early stages (38 and 39). Cultural examinations have indicated that the same organisms are present, although most cases are seen in herds concurrently infected with digital dermatitis. An invasive spirochaete, similar to both digital dermatitis and the spirochaete identified in peracute footrot (contagious ovine digital dermatitis, CODD) in sheep, has been seen in lesions of superfoul. The main difference between foul and superfoul is the speed of onset and the severity of the lesions. Necrosis of the interdigital skin may be seen within twelve hours, with deep necrotic fissures into the dermis within twenty-four. A typical example is seen in Illus. 5.62. Early and aggressive therapy is therefore essential. The treatments used are similar to conventional foul, but at a higher dose and for a longer period. Some benefit has been reported from

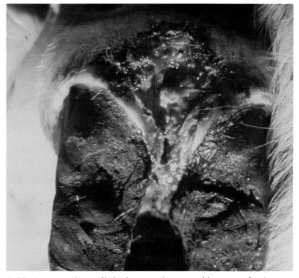

5.62 Extreme interdigital necrosis caused by superfoul.

the use of local anaerobic therapy such as clindamycin, spiramycin and metronidazole. Control is essentially by foot-bathing, as for digital dermatitis.

Digital Dermatitis

First reported in Italy in 1972, digital dermatitis spread across Europe to the Netherlands in the late 1970s and early 1980s and was first reported in the UK in 1985 *(19)*. Combined with white line disease, sole ulcers and 'foul', digital dermatitis is currently one of the four most common causes of lameness in the UK.

Some texts refer to digital (DD) and interdigital dermatitis (IDD) as two separate conditions, but as they are visually so similar and as both respond to the same treatment, it is highly probable that they are identical *(75)*. In this section I have not tried to distinguish the two conditions. Recent DNA typing *(102)* of bacterial isolates from clinical cases has shown that DD and IDD are different manifestations of the same spirochaete infection. Some Dutch authors *(96)* refer to heel necrosis (also known as slurry heel or heel erosion) as interdigital dermatitis. This terminology is not used in the UK or the US.

The typical lesion is first seen as a moist, light grey-brown, exuding area (Illus. 5.63), with matted superficial hairs, situated on the skin at the back of the foot, just between the bulbs of the heels. There is a characteristic foul odour. Cleaning the surface exposes an irregular circular area, covered with diphtheritic debris (Illus. 5.64) and red raw granulation tissue beneath (Illus. 5.65). The lesion is intensely painful to the touch, surprisingly so, considering that it is restricted to the superficial layers of the skin (the epidermis) and produces no swelling of the associated tissues. In this respect it differs from foul, which typically produces swelling around the coronary band extending towards the fetlock. Occasionally, advanced lesions may develop hair-like filaments, as in Illus. 5.66. In North America these are known as 'hairy warts'. Neglected lesions may erode the horn of the heel, producing an under-run heel (Illus. 5.67), and infection may retard the healing of sole ulcers, as in Illus. 5.67.

5.63 Digital dermatitis: moist exudative area with matted hair.

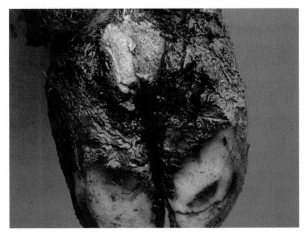

5.64 Digital dermatitis: initial cleaning to reveal diphtheritic material.

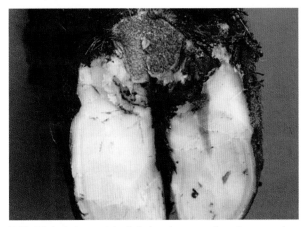

5.65 Digital dermatitis: full cleaning reveals red, raw and extremely painful granulation tissue.

5.66 Neglected cases of digital dermatitis develop into 'hairy warts'.

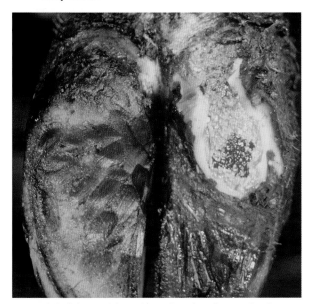

5.67 Digital dermatitis and associated under-run heel.

The characteristic red, inflamed areas may also be seen between the claws (Illus. 5.68) – where it is sometimes termed interdigital dermatitis – on the surface of interdigital hyperplasia swellings (Illus. 5.57) and, less commonly, at the front of the foot (Illus. 5.69). At the front of the foot, erosion of the perioplic horn of the coronary band by digital dermatitis produces a much more severe and protracted lameness, involving under-running of

the front wall of the hoof. The deep, infected axial wall fissures (Illus. 5.41) which are so difficult to trim, may be caused by digital dermatitis lesions originating on the axial coronary band, although there are other causes and these are described earlier in this chapter. Occasionally herd outbreaks of these fissures occur, producing protracted lameness, often with a prolapse of proud flesh through the infected fissure (see Illus. 5.37).

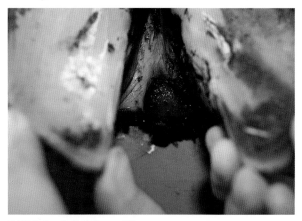

5.68 Interdigital dermatitis.

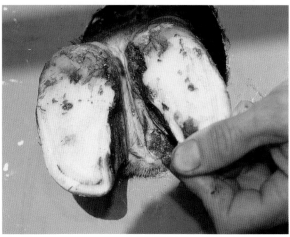

5.69 Digital dermatitis: eroding the perioplic horn at the front of the foot.

The bacterial cause of digital dermatitis

Digital dermatitis is a bacterial infection of the superficial skin; the very prompt response to topical antibiotics indicated quite early on that a bacterial infection was involved. Different invasive spirochaete bacteria of the *Treponema* family *(24, 86, 40)* have been implicated. One is a long, filamentous organism 12 μm long and 3 μm wide and another is a short spirochaete of 5 to 6 μm long and 0.1 μm wide. They are also different on enzymatic and DNA analyses *(102)*. Potential isolates suggested are *Treponema phagedenis, T. vincentii* and *T. denticola*. There are apparently two strains of the organism associated with cattle, and one with sheep, the sheep strain causing the severe form of footrot known as CODD, contagious ovine digital dermatitis. Hence for those few remaining herds that do not have digital dermatitis, it is important for them to avoid close contact with sheep. The Treponemes involved are very similar to those that cause oral infections in man, and, surprisingly since the disease is associated with slurry, they have not been found in bovine faeces.

Environmental factors

Although individual cases of digital dermatitis do occur when cows are out at grass, most herd outbreaks are in housed cattle, especially dairy cows, but heifers, beef animals and even calves can also be affected. Environmental hygiene is the main factor influencing disease, with the most severe outbreaks occurring in housed cattle in winter. Disease is associated with wet conditions, sub-optimal hygiene under-foot and excess exposure to slurry (Illus. 5.70), such as areas where stale slurry accumulates, and excess exposure to slurry. This may be the result of:

- infrequent scraping
- high stocking densities
- insufficient cubicles for the number of cows
- narrow passages, leading to increased accumulation of slurry
- excess standing times
- automatic scrapers
- low bedding use
- larger herds.

One trial found that the only way that they could

5.70 Excess exposure to slurry is one of the major factors associated with digital dermatitis.

transmit dermatitis experimentally was to leave a cow with her foot in a boot full of water for ten days. Trying to transmit the disease onto dry skin simply was not effective. Factors leading to excess standing (and hence increased exposure to slurry) are discussed in the next chapter. It is probably muck rather than mud that leads to disease, because dermatitis is relatively uncommon in the grazing herds of Australia, New Zealand and South America. Despite this, recent research has found that the causative organism is not present in faeces, i.e. it is not a normal gut inhabitant, and as such differs from 'foul'. Several studies have shown that automatic scrapers are associated with an increase in digital dermatitis. The reason is unknown, but it may be because of the wave of slurry produced by the scraper, or because scrapers are often installed in narrow passages, or because scrapers remove the small amount of bedding that falls out of the cubicle and dries the passage. Flush systems have also been associated with an increase in digital dermatitis.

Immunity

Immunity to the disease is probably relatively unimportant – and if this is the case, the prospects for control by vaccination are not good. The evidence for this is that lesions in hind feet are more common than in front feet and, if affected, cattle are more likely to have lesions on both hind feet *(64)*. In addition, it is often the case that the same cow gets dermatitis year after year, suggesting lack of effective immune response and/or recrudescence of latent infections. This may also, of course, be because these are lower-ranking animals which regularly have to spend long periods waiting to be fed and milked, and therefore have longer periods standing in slurry, or because the conformation of their feet is such that their heels drop into the slurry.

The depressed immunity of cows at calving and in very early lactation is likely to be a further factor. Illus. 5.71 shows that the highest incidence of disease is seen in the early lactation period, i.e. the first one to three months after calving, especially if this is during the winter *(64, 22)*, and disease incidence is higher in lactating than dry cows.

Illus. 5.71 shows how DD (yellow bars) and foul (green bars) are found at only a low incidence in dry cows, but the incidence increases rapidly after calving, decreasing again in later lactation. Illus.

5.72 shows a typical early digital dermatitis lesion in a dry cow, seen here as a slight thickening, or hyperkeratinisation, of the skin around the edge of the interdigital cleft. If left, this will soon develop into the raw, open sore of digital dermatitis in early lactation. So, foot-bathing ideally needs to start in the transition group, i.e. two weeks before calving.

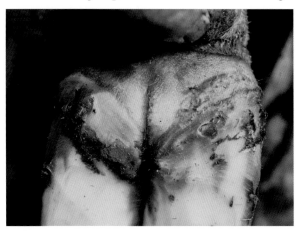

5.72 Early lesions of digital dermatitis are seen as a mild thickening of the skin.

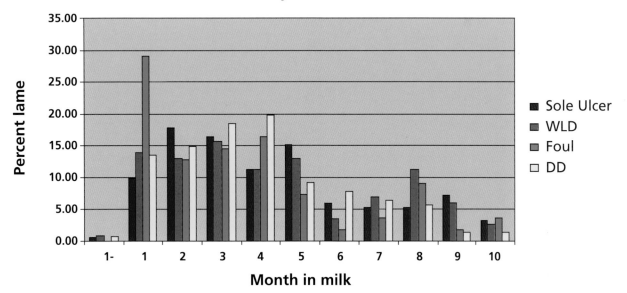

5.71 Note how the incidence of digital dermatitis (yellow bars) and foul (green bars) is low in dry cows, but increases rapidly after calving *(22)*.

The suggested causes for this increase in digital dermatitis in early lactation include:

- Early lactation cows spending longer standing (for milking, feeding, moving and social integration).
- Higher bacterial levels in slurry from higher concentrate diets.
- Faeces are much wetter in early lactation cows.
- Stocking density is often higher.
- Depressed immune response at calving.
- Dry cows may be in straw yards (low DD risk) whereas fresh calvers are more likely to be in cubicles (higher DD risk).

In established herds the disease is commonly seen in purchased animals, or in recently introduced heifers, two to eight weeks after entry into the herd *(12)*. High culling rates and frequent purchase of new stock from a variety of sources probably perpetuates infection in a herd.

Treatment

An individual clinical case of DD (and of mastitis) should be considered a reservoir of infection and a risk to other cows, and as such needs prompt treatment. This is often not done. It is just not acceptable to say that 'a few cows have got a bit of dermatitis', because if left untreated the infection will build up and will soon spread to other cows.

Treatment of individual cases is generally easy. Thoroughly clean the affected area, either with cotton wool and/or by gentle scraping with a hoof knife, and then apply a topical antibiotic. This is best held in place by a dressing for two to three days, thereby giving the antibiotic a good chance to soak in. Intra-mammary antibiotic mastitis tubes have been used and appear to work well, perhaps because they are specifically formulated to penetrate tissue, although in some countries this may require a milk – withhold period.

Copper pastes and other disinfectants are also effective, but may be a little more painful in the early

stages. These latter products cause general tissue damage, i.e. they do not penetrate the tissue and kill bacteria in the same way as antibiotics, and hence treatment may need to be applied for a longer period. In general they are likely to be cheaper. Despite quite severe lameness, one treatment is usually sufficient. The exceptions are lesions at the front of the foot and advanced hairy warts. If the horn-forming tissue of the coronary band is involved, then a vertical fissure (Illus. 5.37) may develop. Dermatitis at this site is hence best treated immediately with both topical and injectable antibiotic. Large 'hairy wart' lesions (Illus. 5.66) may require surgical removal under local anaesthesia.

Herd outbreaks can be treated by the use of foot baths which contain an antibiotic solution (but control is best done by using disinfectants – see next section). The antibiotic originally used was 2–4 g/l oxytetracycline for two or three consecutive milkings. Others have used a single bath containing 6–8 g/l oxytetracycline. Lincospectin is also effective. A 150 g pot containing 33 g lincomycin plus 66 g spectinomycin is sufficient for 150 litres of foot bath at treatment level. Alternatively you can use lincomycin at 400 mg per litre, tylosin, tiamulin or even soluble penicillin. In fact cheap penicillin has been shown to be surprisingly effective against spirochaetes. In some countries antibiotic foot baths are not permitted, and in others there is a statutory milk-withhold period

The best response to foot bathing is obtained by first walking cows into a herring-bone parlour and spraying their feet (and especially their heels) with a pressure hose (Illus. 5.73). Allow these to drain while the other side of the parlour is being filled, before walking the cows through the foot-bath. This takes a surprisingly short time. Usually one bath in antibiotic is sufficient to give temporary relief and it should not interfere with milking. An alternative is to walk cows through a pre-wash water bath before entering a second bath containing the active solution. The initial response can be dramatic, with the number of sore-footed cows declining markedly within twenty-four hours after the foot bath. Unfortunately however, the response is also short lived and a different approach is needed for the *control* of dermatitis.

5.73 Digital dermatitis: spray heels with the pressure hose in the parlour prior to an antibiotic foot-bath treatment.

Prevention and control of digital dermatitis

Digital dermatitis is an infectious disease and, like any other infectious disease such as mastitis, control should be based on environmental hygiene and disinfection, i.e. prevention, and not repeated antibiotic foot-bath treatments.

For example:
- improve the environment to reduce exposure to infection
- treat clinical cases (referred to above)
- regular foot disinfection (teat disinfection is carried out twice-daily for mastitis control).

Environmental hygiene

Environmental hygiene is vital, and some of the more important factors include:

- Passages should be scraped at least twice daily.
- Where possible, allow some cubicle bedding to fall into the passage to reduce exposure of feet to slurry, and to dry up excess moisture.
- Concrete surfaces should be well drained and free from pits and other areas where slurry and water could accumulate.

- Several studies have shown an association between increased digital dermatitis and automatic scrapers. Although scrapers remove slurry more frequently, they also pull a wave of slurry along the passage and this can lead to immersion of the whole foot. Automatic scrapers also remove the small amount of bedding that falls into the passage, and which I think is such an important part of lameness control.

- Buildings should be well ventilated to remove as much humidity as possible. Cows are very 'wet' animals, producing up to 60 litres per day in the urine, faeces, sweat and breath.

- Standing times should be minimised to reduce the contact of feet with slurry. (This is discussed in much more detail in the section on cow time budgets in Chapter Six.)

- Cows should be in comfortable buildings with 3 m wide cubicle passages. Stocking density should be reasonable – a maximum of 90 per cent cubicle occupancy – to ensure that slurry is kept to a minimum and lying times are optimal.

- Provide adequate feed space of 0.4 m per cow, again to minimise standing times.

- Clean and disinfect feet regularly .

- Treat clinical cases as these represent a reservoir of infection to other cows.

Foot-bathing

Regular disinfectant foot-bathing is an extremely important part of the control of digital dermatitis, foul and the other infectious causes of lameness, and it also helps in the control of interdigital 'growths' or 'corns'. Foot-bathing is discussed in this section because it is of such extreme importance in the control of digital dermatitis. Further practical points are given towards the end of Chapter Six, which should be read in conjunction with the following.

Illus. 5.71 showed that both DD and foul increase dramatically after calving. As discussed above, this is probably due to a combination of periparturient immune suppression and increased standing, the latter leading to wet and dirty hooves. *(22)*. Hence the time to start the control of dermatitis is in the late dry period, ideally in the transition cows, before the immune suppression starts. Illus. 5.72 showed low-grade DD in a dry cow. Note the characteristic hyperkeratinisation (a dry thickening) of the skin around the interdigital cleft (the interdigital pouch deep within the cleft being one of the major reservoirs of infection) and at the skin–heel–horn junction on the right heel bulb. It is at this stage of the disease that foot-bathing should start, as this will prevent the development of these minor lesions into the raw open lesion such as Illus. 5.65.

Disinfectant foot baths can be used at this stage, but because disinfectants cause general tissue damage and are not as well absorbed into the epidermis as an antibiotic might be, the disinfectant foot bath *must be applied regularly* to obtain full benefit. The required frequency of bathing will depend on the level of environmental challenge. Many farms now foot bath once a day, every day, for seven days a week, using a fresh 5 per cent formalin or other disinfectant foot bath each time, and are pleased with the results. Other routines such as five days per week, or nine days on and five days off are also used.

The foot bath should be sited in the path of the usual cow flow walkway after the exit to the parlour, but not so close to the parlour that it obstructs the exit or slows milking. Anything that slows milking is unlikely to be repeated regularly! Ideally there should be enough room for at least one whole side of the parlour to exit before the foot bath is reached, thus minimising any disruption to milking. Two foot baths can be placed in series, as in Illus. 6.34, the first to wash the feet, the second with the active chemical. Cows should of course exit into a clean and scraped yard.

Make sure that the floor of the bath is firmly

based and has a comfortable walking surface. If high ridges are present, as in the foot bath in Illus. 5.74, the cows will not like walking through it, and this will lead to reluctance to enter, to increased faecal contamination, and a risk that the teats will become splashed with disinfectant. The ridges are said to splay the claws apart to allow the foot bath to soak into the interdigital space, but this is not necessary because the claws naturally splay when taking weight anyway.

A variety of disinfectant chemicals are used,

5.74 Cows do not like walking on foot baths with ridged surfaces.

each with their own advantages and disadvantages. Formalin (4–5 per cent) is cheap and rapidly degraded in the environment, but unpleasant to handle. Copper sulphate (4–5 per cent, but sometimes up to 20 per cent) is more pleasant to handle but is not degraded in the environment and is more expensive. As copper poisoning is becoming an increasing problem in dairy cows, ideally foot baths should not be simply discarded into the farm drainage system. Zinc sulphate, organic acids and disinfectants such as gluteraldehyde and peracetic acid are also effective.

The method of administration, the frequency of foot-bathing and the cleanliness of the environment are more important than the chemicals used. Some farms have used circulation cleaner with good effect. Put the parlour to wash, allow the chemicals to circulate for five to seven minutes and then, instead of running them to waste, run the liquid into the foot bath. The residual solution has both detergent (for cleaning) and disinfectant properties. It will be effective in a low-risk farm, but stronger disinfectants are needed if the environmental challenge is high. It is this author's belief that within a few years disinfectant foot-bathing will be almost as common as post-milking teat disinfection, carried out at least once a day, especially during housing.

Sponge rubber mats are sometimes used. When the cow stands on the rubber mat the liquid chemical from inside the mat starts to form a pool around the foot and this acts as a bath. The system is easy to use, but it cannot be as effective as a standard foot bath. It is just when the depression produced by the cow's foot begins to fill with chemical that the cow starts to move onto the next stride. Hence the foot does not get as effective a soaking as with a standard bath. However, if the mat is in the base of the foot bath and is covered by 70–80 mm of solution, then this will be of benefit as it increases cow comfort.

A disinfectant foam system is also available, set up such that cows walk through a layer of foam at the entrance to the parlour (Illus. 5.75). The Kovex ™ foam consists of a peracetic acid disinfectant with adhesive properties to improve the adhesion to the hoof plus a skin conditioner and a detergent to assist the foam to penetrate the foot. The foam is deposited at the entrance to the milking parlour, to a depth of 12-14 cm. Cows are therefore standing in the foam while waiting to enter the parlour. They carry foam into the parlour on their feet. This foam remains on the cows' feet during the milking process, so they have their feet bathed in foam for some five to ten minutes.

Trials have suggested that the foam is effective as

5.75 A disinfectant foam can be used at the entrance to the parlour.

a preventive (20), but the disinfectant seems to have a limited effect as a treatment of existing lesions. The system is easy to use and the chemicals are pleasant to handle, with no adverse environmental effects, but by its very definition foam is a liquid with holes in it; hence, its ability to penetrate the interdigital space must be less than when using a liquid bath.

A summary of the main points associated with effective foot-bathing are therefore:

- Use antibiotics for *treatment*, i.e., if there is a high incidence of open raw lesions. The major part of *control* should be the use of disinfectants.

- Start foot bathing early, e.g. in late dry period, and before significant lesions are seen.

- Bath frequently, e.g., daily when using disinfectants.

- Place the bath in a normal 'cow flow' route, and at least one parlour row of cows away from the parlour exit, so that it does not interfere with the flow of cows out of the parlour.

- Ensure that the bath has a good, firm and comfortable base to increase cow flow rates. Avoid baths with high ridges.

- The bath should be easily emptied and cleaned daily.

- Exit cows onto clean concrete and back into clean cubicles
- Consider use of a pre-wash bath.
- A double-width bath increases cow flow rates.

Mud Fever

Mud fever occurs following exposure to cold, wet and muddy conditions. One or more legs may be affected, the first signs being a mild swelling of the leg extending from the top of the hoof to above the fetlock. The skin becomes thickened and the hair encrusted. Hair loss occurs later, exposing the underlying skin, as in Illus. 5.76. In more advanced cases the skin may crack to produce a raw, bleeding area, as seen in Illus. 5.77. Lameness is not severe,

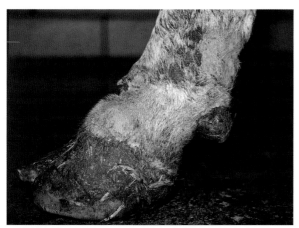

5.76 Mud fever lesions extending up the leg.

5.77 Mud fever: cracked heels.

especially if more than one foot is involved. Affected cows may stand and shake their feet, suggesting that mud fever causes irritation or severe itching.

For treatment, if possible house the cows or at least move them to dry conditions, wash any caked mud from their legs and, when dry, apply a greasy antiseptic ointment. Teat dips or sprays containing a high level of emollient are useful. As infection with the organism *Dermatophilus congolensis* may be involved, a three-day course of injectable antibiotic (e.g., penicillin and streptomycin) may also be beneficial.

Heel Erosion or Slurry Heel

Slurry heel involves both hoof and skin tissue, and is included here for ease of reference. The importance of an intact heel of the correct height for weight bearing, and to maintain the stability of the foot was described in Chapter Three. In housed dairy cows, which stand for long periods in wet, corrosive slurry, the normal smooth, intact horn of the heel becomes eroded and pitted and may become totally worn away. Illus. 5.78 shows early heel erosion, whereas the cow with digital dermatitis in Illus. 5.64 is quite badly affected.

The overall effect of this is to rotate the hoof

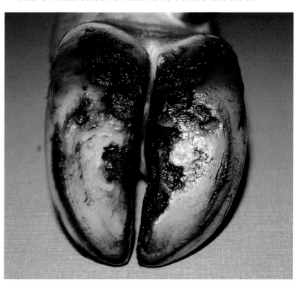

5.78 Early heel necrosis.

backwards. The fetlock drops, the front wall of the hoof forms a much more shallow angle with the horizontal (i.e. decreases from the correct 45 degrees) and the toe may lift from the ground and no longer be weight bearing.

More importantly, internally, the pedal bone rotates back towards the heel, and may pinch the solear corium between its rear edge and the hoof, with resulting pain, lameness and possibly sole ulcer formation. This is shown in Illus. 5.20.

Some hoof trimmers remove the cracks and fissures in the heel. However, because of its extreme importance in weight bearing, I prefer to pare the heel only if it is seriously under-run, or if the heel is so badly eroded that the rear edge of the pedal bone is likely to be directly above the residual ledge of heel horn, as in Illus. 5.20. Note how the horn of the sole has become indented by the pedal bone at 'A', and how the extensively eroded heel is missing at 'B'.

Regular formalin foot baths, and attention to the environment, particularly removing slurry and keeping the feet dry, help to prevent heel erosion.

It is probable that the sprinkling of lime in the cubicles to reduce mastitis incidence also decreases heel erosion, as does the provision of ample bedding. If sufficient bedding is added such that a small quantity is always pulled out and lies in the cubicle passage, this will help to keep feet dry, especially when the cows are standing half in and half out of the cubicle, as they often do. A period of summer grazing is ideal, allowing the heel to recover and form again, ready for the onslaught of the next winter housing period.

CHAPTER SIX

The Causes and Prevention of Lameness

In Chapter Two, page 24, a distinction was made between:

- *pathogenesis*, the changes within the foot that lead to sole ulcers and white line defects, and

- *aetiology*, the changes on the farm which produce the changes within the foot.

This chapter deals with *aetiology*, namely those factors on the farm that can lead to a high incidence of lameness. It is very important that the relevant section of Chapter Two, pages 24 – 32, has been read first to give an understanding of the impact that the various aetiological factors described in the following section have on the internal structure of the foot.

In a herd with a lameness problem, it is unlikely that there will be a single causative factor involved. Lameness is a true example of a multifactorial condition; that is, there will be a number of factors each producing an adverse effect on hoof condition. Each factor on its own may not produce lameness. However, when acting in concert, severe foot problems can result.

Some of the adverse influences on lameness would be very difficult to avoid. Typical examples include:

- Calving, which has been shown to produce solar haemorrhages *(50)* and weaken the white line *(69)*.

- Prolonged standing times on hard concrete surfaces for milking, feeding, drinking, and social interactions *(31)*.

- High levels of yield.

- The high level of feeding required for commercial milk production *(38)*.

However, the effects of the above can be minimised by ensuring that those factors which we are able to influence are optimal for cattle hoof horn production.

Although the influence of nutritional, environmental, management and toxic factors on lameness will be considered separately, it is important that the reader appreciates that in reality all these will be acting in concert. The major importance of calving as a factor, rendering the corium more fragile and therefore more susceptible to nutritional and environmental factors, cannot be overstressed. This is discussed in detail later.

In this chapter the word 'laminitis' is loosely used to include both changes in the sole (where there are papillae but no laminae) and in the white line (which has neither laminae nor papillae) although, as discussed in the section in Chapter Two, generalised changes in the corium (coriitis or coriosis) *(67)* is probably a better term. Detailed scientific reviews of the causes of sole lesions in cattle are available elsewhere *(25, 76, 91)*.

Once the corium has suffered one attack of laminitis, it never fully recovers. Microscopic changes including fibrosis, occlusion of blood vessels and other factors which reduce the functional capacity of the corium to produce healthy hoof often persist *(70)*. This is probably one reason why cows which have been through a laminitic insult have bad feet and an increased risk of lameness for the remainder of their lives. The hooves may remain chronically mis-shapen (Illus. 2.34 is a good example) and have to be regularly trimmed in an attempt to restore reasonable shape and weight-bearing surfaces. Long-term changes to the pedal bone may also occur, including irregular projections (exostoses) from its lower surface (Illus. 5.21), which may lead to discomfort when walking. Hence for lameness, as with so many other diseases of cattle, prevention is essential.

Summary of Changes

There are so many factors affecting lameness that it is difficult to discuss them all in detail and at the same time, to show how each factor interacts with the others. To help overcome this difficulty, in this chapter I intend first to outline the major changes that I believe lead to an increase in lameness, then deal with each one of these factors in a little more detail, and finally, at the end of the chapter, summarise the main points that have been made.

The major factors affecting lameness can be listed as:

- calving
- changes in diet
- excess standing
- changes in management.

Illus. 6.1 shows one horn from 'Pinky', a 13-year-old cow from Bulawayo in the south of Zimbabwe. In her thirteen years all that was required of this cow was to graze 5,000 acres of veldt (pasture land) and periodically have a calf, so it was not a particularly stressful life. However, note that there are six rings on her horns, one for each calving. At calving, the rate of horn growth slows down and yet for the post-partum dairy heifer, especially, hoof wear considerably increases.

Sole thickness = rate of growth minus rate of wear. The net result of reduced growth and increased wear at calving is that the sole can become much thinner, sometimes to the point of causing lameness.

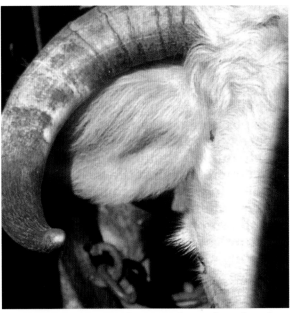

6.1 The rings on a cow's horns are due to disruption of horn formation at the time of calving. Similar changes occur within the feet.

The increased rate of hoof wear will be due to:

- Standing to be milked – and it is the freshly calved heifer (or the lame cow) which is often last to enter the parlour.

- Standing to be fed – again, the freshly calved heifer often has to wait until others have finished before she can feed, especially if there is insufficient feed space available.

- Standing on concrete – many heifers have not been adequately adapted to concrete prior to calving. They must learn to stand differently, with their hind feet 'base wide'.

- Standing because she cannot find an empty cubicle to lie in, or perhaps she has never been trained to use cubicles before, and hence does not know how to use them.

- Standing while she establishes herself at the appropriate level in the social hierarchy of the herd. This is especially important when the freshly calved heifer is mixed with the main herd after calving.

All this increased standing occurs at a time when hoof growth is minimal, with the net result that the sole gets thinner and the corium is more likely to become bruised. At the same time there is increased movement of the pedal bone within the hoof, and her diet changes to a high concentrate ration, which further predisposes to disruption of the normal function of the corium. Although often no changes are visible in the foot at this stage, they are occurring deep within the corium, and two to three months later they will appear as an increase in lameness. In addition, increased standing means more exposure to slurry, and this increases the risk of infectious disorders such as digital dermatitis and foul. This is classically demonstrated in Illus. 6.2 *(22)* which shows the number of lame cows per month after calving in a study involving 1,109 cow years on trial. In the first month after calving approximately 22 cows were recorded as lame, in the second month there were 50 lame cows, and lameness peaked in the third month after calving when almost 60 animals were affected. Some might think that the high level of lameness in the third month after calving is caused by peak yield and cows coming bulling, and this is probably a contributory factor. However, the stresses and

changes in the foot associated with calving will be of primary importance to produce this peak.

In the following sections each of the factors at calving will be examined in more detail. These include:

- changes at calving
- nutritional factors
- decreased lying times
- increased hoof wear
- reduced horn growth
- increased movement of the pedal bone within the hoof
- immune suppression and increased risk of periparturient diseases
- changes in housing and floor surfaces
- changes in management and social integration.

Changes at Calving

Many people have described an association between calving and the production of sole haemorrhage and other causes of coriosis/ laminitis *(50, 69, 76)*, and lameness generally is more common during the first few months after calving *(22, 89)*. The precise cause of this is unknown, but the rings on a cow's horns indicate

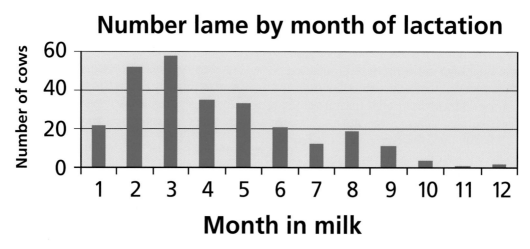

6.2 The pattern of lameness.
This diagram shows how the incidence of lameness increases after calving, reaching a peak two to three months later. As the sole is around 10 mm thick and horn grows at 5 mm per month, this is precisely what would be expected if the damage was caused at calving *(22 ex L. Green)*.

that there is a disruption in horn formation in every cow at calving. The main changes at calving are: (i) reduced horn growth and (ii) increased movement of the pedal bone.

Reduced Horn Growth

This is clearly shown in the cow in Illus. 6.1. Although thirteen years old, she has had only six calves and hence the six rings on her horns. If you look at a bull's horns you will not find any rings (unless he has been very sick at some stage). This disruption in horn formation also occurs in the foot and it means that at the time of calving the corium is very fragile and even more susceptible to bruising. Yet this is often the time when many other stresses are imposed on the cow, for example a sudden change to an 'acidosis type' ration, or an introduction into a new (and perhaps uncomfortable) cubicle house, or a change into a new and larger social group, all of which are in themselves important causes of foot problems.

The cause of the disruption of horn formation at calving is unknown. The blood levels of haptoglobulins and other acute phase proteins (which are indicators of inflammation) increase at parturition, and the signal for parturition to start is in fact the intra-uterine release of cortisone by the calf. As administration of cortisone to horses can induce laminitis, perhaps it is the increase in foetal cortisone which is important.

Another theory is that it is the start of lactation rather than the process of calving which is involved. Sulphur-containing amino acids such as cysteine and methinione are needed for both keratin formation (see Chapter Two) and for milk production. The sudden start of milk production, draining all the sulphur amino acids away from horn formation and into lactation, could result in a short period of poor-quality horn formation. There is also a drop in serum protein levels (albumin and globulin) around the time of calving. This is one of the factors that leads to oedema (the accumulation of fluid) under the skin of the udder and belly: perhaps similar changes occur within the foot, with stasis of blood leading to anoxia and poor horn formation, as described in Chapter Two.

Increased Movement of the Pedal Bone

The suspension of the rear edge of the pedal bone on three fat pads, supported within the pedal suspensory ligament was described in Chapter Two and Illus. 2.21 and 2.22. In the two weeks prior to calving there is an increase in the levels of an enzymes termed relaxin and 'hoofase'. *(94)* This activates the MMPs responsible for the suspension of the front of the pedal bone (Illus. 2.28) and, combined with an increase in flexibility of the pedal suspensory ligament, there is an increased movement of the bone within the hoof. This produces an increased risk of damage to the corium.

The greater flexibility lasts approximately from two weeks before calving to two weeks after calving; hence it is over this period that the cow is particularly susceptible to damage. Mastitis, metritis and other toxic changes are also more common immediately after calving.

Calving or Feeding?

Changes in management and feeding are also of importance. For example, in one experiment ten steers were housed, fed and managed with a group of ten pregnant heifers of the same age. As the heifers calved, they changed housing and were transferred onto a production ration. The steers followed suit – although obviously only the heifers calved! Both steers and heifers in the group showed sole haemorrhages, but the haemorrhages were much more severe in the heifers. This shows that nutrition and environment must be significant factors in addition to calving.

A small but increasing number of dairy farmers are attempting to minimise stress by keeping heifers in straw yards or in a separate heifer group for the first four to six weeks after calving *(43)*. Most agree that this leads to:

- Decreased lameness, because lying times are increased and so there is less trauma on an inherently fragile corium.

- Increased yields, presumably because the heifers are more comfortable and under less stress. There will also be less competition at feeding.

- Improved cubicle acceptance when the heifers are eventually introduced into cubicles. This is perhaps the most surprising aspect of the system, but probably emphasises the fact that calving is a much more stressful event than we allow for.

Poor Circulation and Fluid Pooling

Changes in the blood circulation around the time of calving often lead to a pooling of fluid. This is commonly seen in the udder as excess oedema or 'nature'. A similar pooling of fluid occurs in the corium, leading to softer horn production and, in more extreme cases, to haemorrhage, horn separation and sole ulcers.

The problem is made worse by the fact that heifers, especially, have been shown to spend longer periods standing during the two weeks prior to calving and the two weeks following calving *(65)*. Disease at this stage, leading to yet further pooling of fluid in the corium, is therefore particularly important. Standing times are referred to in more detail later in this chapter.

The maintenance of good blood flow within the foot is assisted by exercise. Make sure that cows at calving are not totally confined to calving boxes and, if they are sick, encourage them to move around a little. This does not, of course, mean putting them back into the main herd where they would have to compete for food and priority in the pecking order.

Nutritional Factors

The normal rumen pH is around 6.5. After a feed of concentrate in the parlour this may fall to pH 6.0, or even 5.5 if a large intake of a high-starch (high-energy) concentrate is received. Starch is fermented by the ruminal micro organisms into lactic acid and the fall in rumen pH is known as rumen acidosis. Substantial quantities of lactic acid can be converted into propionate and then into glucose; however, if overloading occurs, lactic acid leaks into adjacent blood vessels. Initially it is buffered by bicarbonate, but increasing amounts of lactic acid produce a metabolic acidosis. This means that the blood itself starts to become too acid (whereas in rumen acidosis the changes are confined to the rumen.) It is these changes of metabolic acidosis that are thought to affect the corium.

It is generally accepted that high-starch, low-fibre diets, producing ruminal acidosis, are the most important nutritional factors in the production of laminitis, and can result in lameness due to sole ulcers and white line abscesses. The term SARA, subacute rumen acidosis, is often used to describe the changes associated with such diets. Rations should be formulated with a concentrate: forage ratio no greater than 60:40. Even at this level, problems can occur, especially if the concentrate is high in starch or if the silage is precision-chopped, high-quality and low in fibre, giving an overall neutral detergent fibre level in the ration of less than 40 per cent.

Such diets benefit from the inclusion of 1–2 kg of hay or straw, either mixed in a complete ration, or simply made available on free access. It is surprising how much hay or straw fresh-calved cows will eat if it is available on free access, and dry fibrous foods seem to stimulate better salivation and rumination than moist forages such as silage. The long fibre of big bale silage is a useful alternative, as is the longer fibre content of whole crop silage. I accept that feeding hay or straw will decrease the energy concentration of the diet and could lead to under-feeding, but this has to be balanced against the risk of rumen acidosis leading to rumen atony (= decreased rumen contractions) and consequently to depressed dry matter intakes.

Other factors leading to SARA include cows 'sorting' the ration, i.e. selecting and overeating the concentrate component of a TMR (this can be a consequence of inadequate mixing), or over-mixing in the feeder wagon, which reduces fibre length. The effect of over-mixing varies with the type of feeder wagon.

One of the biggest errors is to allow cows to run out of food and get too hungry. When the food does arrive the cows over-eat (often called 'slug feeding') which itself can produce rumen acidosis. Hence, frequent feeds during the day, or frequent 'push ups' of the ration, are needed to encourage regular feed intakes.

Cows affected by rumen acidosis show a range of clinical signs, depending on severity. These include:

- reduced food intakes (associated with poor rumen movements or even total atony).
- reduced yields
- low milk fat
- loose faeces, often yellow/green in colour, and with an acrid smell (Illus. 6.3)
- matted sweaty coats (Illus. 6.4)
- panting (trying to breathe off the excess acid)
- regurgitation of the cud (Illus. 6.5)
- tail-swishing due to vaginal irritation from acid urine.

Rumen acidosis is, to a certain extent, a self-perpetuating process. Decreasing rumen pH decreases rumen motility, which in turn depresses appetite. Consequently, dry matter intake falls. The cow that has over-eaten concentrate in the parlour will therefore probably eat less forage, thus

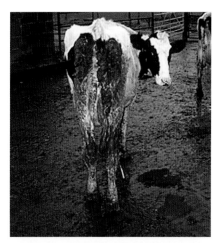

6.4
Rumen acidosis: affected cows often have matted coats. This heifer is also 'tucked up' in the abdomen and she is scouring.

6.5   Cud regurgitation is a further sign of rumen acidosis.

exacerbating rumen acidosis. This is particularly important immediately after calving, when the cow's appetite is depressed generally and reduction in forage intake is often made worse by increased concentrate intakes. The substitution rate (the decrease in kg silage DM eaten per 1.0 kg extra concentrate given) is much greater in early lactation, and hence increased concentrate intakes depress forage consumption. Studies have shown that lush grazing can also produce rumen acidosis, especially when starch levels in the grass are high.

B Vitamin (Biotin) Synthesis

One of the consequences of rumen acidosis is thought to be reduced B vitamin synthesis in the rumen. Although the ruminant has traditionally been considered to be self-sufficient in B vitamins,

6.3   Faeces: loose (right) and 'normal'. Loose faeces are often a sign of rumen acidosis.

recent studies have shown that supplementing high-producing cows with B vitamins can produce a range of performance benefits, including increased yields and reduced lameness *(18)*. In vitro studies have shown that with high concentrate diets producing rumen acidosis, biotin synthesis was reduced from 1.5 to 0.3 µg per day. *(37)*.

In an extensive split herd intervention study involving over 1,100 cow lactations in five UK dairy herds, supplementation with 20 mg/day biotin significantly halved the incidence of lameness caused by white line lesions *(54)*. In cows of fifth lactation and above, where the incidence of white line disease is higher, supplementation with biotin produced a 3.5 fold reduction in lameness from white line lesions.

Survival analysis demonstrated that supplementation needed to be given for 130 days before any difference in the two groups was seen *(54)*. This is to be expected, as it will take at least two months for hoof improved with biotin to reach the bearing surface of the foot. These results do not mean that every cow should be supplemented with biotin, of course, but rather that cows should, if at all possible, be fed to avoid rumen acidosis. However, as other trials have also shown that biotin increases yields by around 1 - 2 litres per day, the supplementation should be self-financing.

Several other authors have reported a relationship between biotin and different types of lameness including sole ulcers and heel erosion *(26)*. A Japanese study found a relationship between blood biotin levels and cattle lameness, and recommended dietary supplementation with biotin *(60)*.

Rumen Bacterial Endotoxins

As stated previously, the precise way in which rumen acidosis causes coriosis/laminitis is still unknown. One of the suggestions is that a change in rumen fermentation causes the release of bacterial endotoxins (endotoxins are breakdown products of dead bacteria) which, when absorbed, stimulate histamine release by the cow *(4)*.

Histamine damages blood vessels, thus disturbing the delicate blood flow control mechanisms within the hoof. Pooling of blood occurs and blood clots (thrombosis) may form. These processes are described in more detail in on pages 28–9.

It is probable that damage to the arteriovenous anastomoses, the minute connections between arteries and veins which exist at the base of the laminae and papillae, is involved in the basic changes of laminitis *(100)*. If there is insufficient blood flow in the corium, this leads to inadequate supplies of oxygen and sulphur-containing amino acids, both of which are essential for horn formation. It has been shown experimentally that changes occur in the corium in as little as two hours after injecting lactic acid into the rumen *(53)*. Within seven days there were microscopic areas of separation between the horn and the horn-forming layers (between the stratum corneum and stratum germinativum), see page 13. If allowed to progress, this could lead to sole ulcers or even total horizontal fissures, as described in Chapter Five.

Bacterial endotoxins are not only formed in the rumen. They can also arise from bacterial death following acute mastitis or metritis (uterine infection) and both conditions therefore require adequate treatment in order to prevent subsequent hoof disorders. This is discussed at the end of this chapter.

Frequency of Feeding

Frequency of feeding can also have an effect on rumen acidosis. On twice-daily milking, parlour concentrate intakes should be restricted to 8–10 kg per day, i.e. a maximum of 5 kg per feed, and ideally 4 kg per feed, or less. There is a high risk of laminitis/coriosis at parlour intakes of 12 kg per day and above, especially if a high-starch product is used.

The practice of putting out feeds of concentrate (or maize gluten, palm kernel, etc.) during morning milking should also be discouraged. Distributing the feed when the cows are shut in for milking may be easier, but it means that the cows will then be faced with a second feed of concentrates as soon as they leave the parlour. Some of the high-yielders may not eat any of the out-of-parlour concentrate and hence yields suffer, while the stale milkers get over-fat. Those fresh calvers which do eat the concentrate run the risk of an even more severe acidosis and hence feet and fertility may both be affected. Concentrates containing increased levels of digestible fibre will help.

It is far better for the cows to consume concentrates equally throughout the day, either as a TMR complete diet through a forage wagon, or as one to two additional feeds outside the parlour.

Dietary Fat

Avoid high-fat rations. Levels of fat in excess of 5 per cent of the total dry matter can lead to depressed forage digestion due to both the ruminal micro-organisms and fibre particles becoming coated with fat. This could produce a secondary acidosis. High levels of unsaturated fatty acids (PUFAs, polyunsaturated fatty acids) can have a particularly severe effect and, in the extreme, produce death.

Changes in Diet at Calving

Sudden changes in diet are dangerous, especially if from low- to high-concentrate rations. This may occur at calving. Ideally, cows should be fed a small quantity (to avoid their becoming too fat) of the production ration prior to calving, to acclimatise the rumen micro organisms and then, following calving, the ration should be built up slowly, so that peak concentrate intakes are not reached until three to six weeks into lactation.

The recent trend towards shorter dry periods, such as 40-45 days, where a single high-straw ration is fed throughout the dry period, i.e. from drying off to calving, has resulted in a marked reduction in milk fever, retained placenta, metritis and other post-partum disorders. This may well show benefits for lameness. Do not over-feed after calving. Very high feed intakes simply boost milk production and this puts the cow under even more metabolic stress. An increasing number of producers now move freshly

calved cows into the low-yielder group for one to two weeks until they have got over the stress of calving. Others offer hay with the production ration (Illus. 6.6). There is a natural reduction in the rate of rumination around calving. The provision of long fibre, such as hay, is one of the best ways of stimulating rumination after calving.

Flat-rate feeding was once popular, whereby

6.6 Offering hay to fresh calvers will reduce the risk of rumen acidosis.

cows were fed a maximum level of concentrate (usually 8–9 kg per day), irrespective of level of yield. In some herds this may have helped to reduce foot problems by restricting peak concentrate intakes. However, in other herds where all the concentrate is fed outside the parlour and cows are introduced immediately onto maximum ration following an all-forage restricted diet in the dry period, flat-rate feeding may be counter-productive.

This might explain why some people *(103)* have associated an increased incidence of lameness with flat-rate feeding herds. This is a good example of the multifactorial influences on lameness, discussed in the introduction to this chapter.

It is the composition of the diet and not simply the overall energy intake which affects the incidence of laminitis. Table 6.1 (68) shows two groups of cows, one of which (A) was fed a high-fibre diet and the other (B) a low-fibre and high-concentrate diet. Both rations had the same overall crude protein (CP) content and both groups of cows achieved a similar total daily energy intake (MJ/kg), although the high-fibre group clearly needed a greater dry matter intake to do so.

The high incidence of both laminitis and sole ulcers in the low-fibre group (B) is striking. Despite regular foot trimming, group B also had a higher incidence of solear overgrowths. In this trial, pre-calving feeding had no effect.

Similar results (Table 6.2) have been reported (83) in a trial which continued over two lactations. The differences in the concentrate and forage diets were greater in the second lactation, presumably because of an additive effect of first-lactation insults.

High-concentrate feeding is not the only factor involved in the production of white line abscess and sole ulcers, however. There has been a high incidence of both conditions in a herd fed a low level of concentrate on a flat-rate system, giving an overall concentrate: forage ratio of only 20:80 (9).

Conversely, others (78) have reported no significant increases in hoof lesions despite short periods of extreme over-feeding, so extreme that it

	ME (MJ/kg)	CP (g/kg)	No. showing clinical laminitis	sole ulcers
Group A fed a high-fibre diet	10.8	158	2(8%)	2(8%)
Group B fed a low-fibre diet	11.1	157	17(68%)	16(64%)

Number of cows in Group A=26 and in Group B=25

Table 6.1. Effect of high- and low-fibre diets on laminitis and sole ulcers (68)

	1st lactation No. of cows	No. treated	(%)	2nd lactation No. of cows	No. treated	(%)
Experiment 1						
High-concentrate group	46	26	(58)	29	19	(66)
High-roughage group	47	14	(30)	35	11	(31)
	0.005 <P<0.01			0.005 <P<0.01		
Experiment 2						
High-concentrate group	33	8	(24)	14	12	(85)
High-roughage group	30	5	(17)	20	6	(28)
	NS	P<0.005				

Significance between groups statistically tested by Pearson's x2 test using the hypothesis that yes or no sole ulcer is equally distributed among both groups. NS Not significant.

Table 6.2. The number of cows treated for sole ulcers on high-concentrate and high-fibre diets (83).

In Experiment 1 concentrates and forage (roughage) were fed separately and at the end of the first lactation high-concentrate-fed cows were switched onto a high-forage diet and vice versa.

In Experiment 2 concentrates and forage were fed as a complete diet to all cows and there was no change at the end of the first lactation.

was enough to make some cows clinically ill for a few days.

Dietary Protein

It has been suggested that diets high in protein possibly cause an increased incidence of lameness (8, 71) perhaps due to high levels of ammonia produced in the rumen (103). However, this is not thought to be a common problem. The very high protein intakes in association with spring grazing certainly are not always a major cause, although it has been shown that the high carbohydrate in lush grazing can produce rumen acidosis. It is possible that high protein winter rations are associated with high concentrate intakes and it is in fact starch overload and not excess protein which is the factor involved. High protein diets do stimulate high early lactation yields, and it is possible that the increased metabolic problems associated with increased yields could increase lameness. Diets giving an overall crude protein of above 17 per cent are best avoided.

High incidences of lameness are often associated with grass silage, especially if the silage is wet and poorly fermented. Whether this is due to toxic substances (possibly amines) in the silage having a direct effect on the vasculature of the corium, or whether it is simply due to the fact that feeding such silage reduces overall forage intake, thus altering the concentrate: forage ratio, is not known (50).

Milk Yield

Feed intake influences milk yield, and many studies have shown a relationship between increasing yield and lameness. In one study, involving 1,109 cow years on trial and 750 cases of lameness, animals that went lame produced on average approximately 400 litres per lactation more than their counterparts who did not go lame (49). Feeding for higher yields is likely to lead to increased levels of lameness, therefore, but it is not known whether this is due to dietary factors or to increased standing times associated with increased feed intakes, or both.

Feeding During Rearing

In heifers, high levels of concentrates, and especially a sudden change from low to high concentrate even during the rearing period (less than 18 months old), have been shown to produce laminitis (50).

Feed intakes to produce growth rates of 800 g perday and above were found to produce sole haemorrhages in heifers. This is particularly interesting, considering that over the past ten to fifteen years there has been a marked change towards calving dairy heifers at two years old. To achieve this, increased growth rates which require higher concentrate feeding have been necessary. Could this be one reason why there has been an increase in lameness over the same period?

Some herds have recently reduced concentrate intakes for heifer rearing in an attempt to alleviate this. Provided that forage is made freely available, growth rates do not appear to suffer. Ration palatability, and hence overall dry matter intakes, can be maximised by incorporating brewers' grains and similar high-digestibility fibre feeds. Post-calving dry matter intakes may be higher in heifers which have been reared on high-forage diets.

Cow Condition

Cow condition at calving is also important. Cows over-fat at calving have reduced appetites, particularly for forage (46), and are therefore more prone to developing metabolic disorders, mastitis, rumen acidosis and laminitis. Ideally, cows should be fed to be dried off at condition score 2.5–3.0 and maintained in this condition until calving.

If the cow is over-fat at drying off it is difficult to achieve significant weight loss during the dry period. A diet of ad lib barley straw plus 0.5 kg of a high-protein concentrate (the Atkins diet for cows!) will lead to weight loss, but of course it is highly inefficient in terms of feed utilisation to allow cows to gain excess weight and then force them to lose it again. It is also vital to avoid rapid weight loss in the late dry period otherwise quite severe metabolic problems could result, which could in itself predispose to lameness. Silage should never be fed ad lib to dry cows unless weight gain is specifically required.

Zinc, Sulphur and Trace Elements

Specific nutrients have been suggested to increase the hardness of hoof horn, but documented evidence of their effectiveness is often contradictory and their importance compared with other factors is likely to be limited.

Soft horn is said to have a higher water content and lower zinc and sulphur content than hard horn. Supplementation with 3 g per day zinc oxide has been suggested as being beneficial, although zinc methionine may be better absorbed and more efficiently incorporated into the hoof. Chelated mineral supplements are claimed to increase mineral uptakes, but others say that this is no better than increasing the base amount of mineral in the diet. There is a risk that over-supplementation with zinc or sulphur will induce copper deficiency.

Environmental Factors

Standing Times and Time Budgets

Environment has a major impact on lameness, in that cows which spend long periods standing are often the worst affected. Long periods of standing produce increased pressure on the sole, thereby leading to physical traumatic damage, often manifest as haemorrhage in the typical sole ulcer site. In addition, if a cow stands but does not move, the delicate blood flow mechanisms within the foot (see Chapter One) are put under stress, the blood pools and stagnates and horn formation is adversely affected.

To put lying times into perspective, it is necessary to look at the cow's overall daily routine. This is often referred to as a 'time budget'.

Ideally, a cow should spend between twelve and fourteen hours per day lying down *(27, 55, 59)*. To achieve this, cubicles must be well designed and well bedded, and heifers must be trained to use cubicles prior to calving. There are a number of other things a cow must do each day. These are:

- lie in a cubicle to rest
- stand to be milked
- stand to be fed

- stand to drink
- stand to socialise, and this category includes both agonistic behaviour, when the cow establishes herself in the ranking of social order, and activities such as grooming and oestrus behaviour.

Milking times vary enormously between herds. Some herds are good at minimising standing times. The group to be milked is only brought out of the cubicles when milking starts, someone else feeds, scrapes the passages and applies clean bedding, and the cows are then allowed back in almost immediately after milking. In some herds standing times may be as little as thirty minutes per milking (Illus. 6.7). In other herds I have seen systems where perhaps all three groups of cows are brought out for milking at the same time. When milked, all three groups are then left to stand until the third group has stood for thirty minutes, waiting for the teat canal to close as a mastitis preventive, something which I think is, in most instances, unecessary, and even counter-productive. In this situation, standing times can be as high as three hours per milking, or six hours per day.

6.7 Try to minimise the time cows stand waiting to be milked. Note that all their heads are down, indicating comfort. There is no evidence of excess use of the backing gate.

Provided that passages are clean and that cubicles have been re-bedded, I think that it is better to allow the cows to walk back past food and have full access to the cubicles immediately after milking. This is especially the case if they have also been through a disinfectant foot bath, so their feet are cleaner anyway. The majority of the cows will stop and eat some of the fresh food that has been put out (or perhaps just pushed up), and those that are so desperate to get back to the cubicles to lie down, perhaps because they are sick or have bad feet, should be allowed to do so.

Time budgets can be difficult where units are managed single-handed. One man has to get the cows out of the cubicles, then scrape the passages, then apply fresh bedding, and perhaps even put out fresh feed, before he can start milking. Cows may have already been standing for one hour before milking starts. If the parlour then has a slow throughput, and the milker wishes to keep cows standing until thirty minutes after the last cow has been milked, overall standing times can easily again increase to three hours per milking, six hours per day.

Similar considerations apply to feed areas. Cows spend over six hours per day standing to feed, the longest single activity that requires standing. There should be ample feed and enough space available to allow all cows to feed at the same time. For Friesian Holsteins this is at least 0.6 m of trough space per cow, and for the pre-calving transition and fresh-calver groups, where there is more mixing of cows, greater social interaction, cows with larger abdomens and often slightly uncomfortable cows due to parturition, space is best increased to 0.8 m per cow.

If there is insufficient space available, it is the lower-ranking cows, namely the fresh-calved

heifers and the lame cows, that have to wait until the others have fed. Of course, these are the very animals for which we would like to minimise standing times.

Even the design of the feed barrier can have an effect. It is said that if cows stand obliquely to feed, as in Illus. 6.8, then the top rail is too far back and the cow is not comfortable when feeding. In this picture the rail has already been fixed onto the far side of the upright to give extra space. Ideally the base of the feed face should be 300 mm above the floor standing surface, again to give better access. Improved trough access produces shorter feeding times, and this in turn allows cows to lie for longer.

Drinking and socialising takes around one hour per day, although this can be much longer for the freshly calved cow who is trying to establish her rank in the social order. It has been shown *(35)* that when a cow is introduced into a fresh group of animals the number of aggressive interactions increases during the first three days after mixing. Milk yields fall by 3–5 per cent. Typically the 'moved cow' is involved in an average of ten aggressive interactions per hour, approximately

6.8　It has been suggested that if cows stand side-on to feed, as in this picture, the feed trough will not be comfortable. Note that here the top rail has already been moved to inside the stanchion upright to provide better access to feed.

half of which are physical (bunting, pushing or fighting) and half are simply threatening. This increase in physical interactions obviously has an influence on the other activities of the day, and will clearly increase standing times.

So far in the daily time budget we have:

- 14 hours lying
- 6 hours feeding
- 1 hour drinking and socialising/establishing the social order
- 3 hours milking.

This is achievable, but certainly does not allow the cow much free time. If milking times are prolonged, however, say to three hours per milking – six hours per day – then lying times are immediately reduced to a maximum of eleven hours per day. This assumes that there is ample feed space, that the freshly calved heifers have been trained to use cubicles and that the cubicles are sufficiently comfortable to encourage the cows to lie down during the time they have available. If feed space is limited, then the lower-ranking cows, the lame cows and the fresh-calvers will spend time standing waiting to be fed.

Lying Times

Anything which discourages a cow from lying will obviously lead to a further increase in standing times. This includes a wide range of factors such as cubicle bedding, cubicle design, cubicle stocking rates/occupancy levels, and the overall atmosphere in the building. Housing that is excessively hot or humid will dramatically decrease lying times (and feed intakes), predisposing to both lameness and mastitis. Heat stress is becoming an important condition in total confinement housing systems and is referred to in detail in a later section on environment.

Cubicle Bedding

Table 6.3 shows the amount of time cows spent lying down each day in cubicles which were of identical design but differently bedded. Non-

yielding surfaces such as the bare concrete and hard rubber mat produced much lower lying times.

Another trial *(31)* comparing two identically managed herds, both housed in identical cubicles, showed that using more straw bedding in the cubicles increased the amount of lying time, that more first-lactation heifers* went into the cubicle house and that the time between entry and lying down was shortened. This led to a significant decrease in the incidence of lameness from sole ulcers and white line disease in the herd where ample straw bedding was in use.

Type of cubicle bed	Length of time cows spent resting each day
Bare concrete	7.2 hours
Insulated concrete screed	8.1 hours
Hard rubber mat	9.8 hours
Chopped straw on concrete	14.1 hours
Proprietary cow cushion	14.4 hours

Table 6.3. Cow resting times related to cubicle bedding *(11)*

Whatever the cubicle design, therefore, adequate bedding, whether it be mats, mattresses, sand, sawdust or deep straw, is essential for comfort. Mats and mattresses must be at least lightly covered with sawdust or straw to keep them dry and to reduce the risk of friction sores developing on legs (an extreme example is shown in Illus. 6.9) and to reduce the risk of mastitis. Second-hand quarry belting, fixed with its worn surface downwards, makes inexpensive cubicle matting, but it is very hard and by no means as comfortable as mattresses or deep straw. Deep straw is obviously ideal, but it can sometimes be difficult to get clean straw to adhere to a concrete cubicle base, and straw increases the risk of mastitis.

* Heifers are more likely to be bullied by cows and therefore less likely to enter a cubicle house if there is no escape route. They are also more prone to sole ulcers and hence this is the reason why the researchers specifically targeted this group.

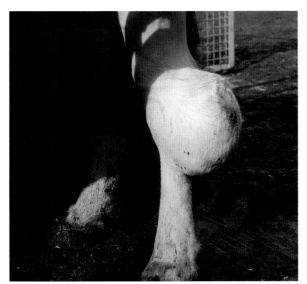

6.9 Hock sores such as this are the result of excess friction from the cubicle bed.

cubicles. One study *(34)* showed that although there was no overall difference in lying times between mattresses and sand cubicles of identical design, there was a much lower incidence of lameness in the sand cubicles. This was thought to occur because, as they started to go lame, the lame cows, especially, found sand easier to lie in. The increased lying times that this produced decreased the overall incidence of lameness.

It is very important to use sand with low clay content so that it does not 'ball' when handled. Sand with a high clay content tends to become compacted and go hard when the cows lie on it, especially if there is milk, urine or other dampness on the beds. Washed sand drains well and is easy to handle. Most farms simply apply clean sand to the front of the cubicle once each week, and then scrape back fresh sand twice a day at each milking as they clean off the back of the cubicle. Compared to the twice-daily bedding that is required with straw, the labour input is clearly much less.

Deep sand beds are increasing in popularity although it can cause problems with slurry handling (Illus. 6.10). Being inert, sand does not support bacterial growth. Provided it is deep enough, cows find sand comfortable, allowing easier lying and standing movements in the

The amount of bedding needed depends on the base of the cubicle (whether concrete, mat or mattress), and Table 6.4 gives approximate

6.10 Deep sand cubicles with ample side lungeing space are ideal for cow comfort.

Material	Requirement (per cow per day)	Typical costs (2007) (per tonne)	(per cow per day)	DM
Sand	8 kg	£12	9.6 p	Wet 81% Dry 97%
Sawdust (kiln dried)	1.5 kg	£100 (bags)	15.0 p	87%
		£75 (bulk)	11.2 p	
Sawdust (fresh)	2.0 kg	£35	7.0 p	69%
Straw (cubicle)	2.5 kg	£40	10 p	85%
Straw (yard)	10 kg	£40	25 p	85%
Paper waste	2.2 kg	£55	12.3 p	92%
Lime	50 g	£180 (bag)	1.0 p	100%

Table 6.4. A comparison of bedding material requirements, costs and dry-matter content.

guidelines only. The dry-matter values are from one small survey only; the costs are approximate, and apply to 2007 UK values. A recent alternative to sand is to use waste ash from the new power stations fired by cardboard, paper and wood. This provides good comfort and has a very high pH which inhibits bacterial growth, although care is needed because it may result in teat skin damage if used in conjunction with certain dips.

The dry-matter content of sawdust is of interest. Sawdust from fresh-cut wood had a dry-matter content of only 69 per cent (i.e. 31 per cent of the bedding was water!) Kiln-dried sawdust was 87 per cent DM and a proprietary waste paper product had 92 per cent DM. Straw yards provide the best environment for lameness prevention, but bedding costs are high and there is a much greater mastitis risk.

Ideally, sufficient bedding should be provided such that a small amount is pulled out by the movement of the cow to lie in the cubicle passage at the base of the kerb (Illus. 6.11). This is not wasted bedding. It is very useful as it acts:

- As a shock absorber for the hind feet when the cow reverses from the cubicle and steps down onto the passage.

6.11   Use enough straw bedding so that some falls out into the gutter, giving the cow a soft and dry standing area for her hind feet.

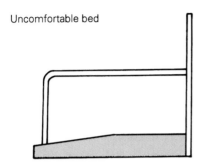
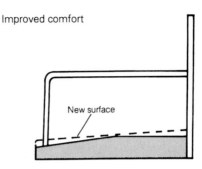

Uncomfortable bed   Improved comfort

New surface

6.12   Cubicles with a change in slope in the middle of the bed are much less comfortable.

- As a cleaning material, preventing slurry heel and digital dermatitis.
- As a soft surface for those cows that in every herd stand half in and half out of the cubicle when they are ruminating.
- To keep feet dry and therefore hooves harder.

Real luxury accommodation, provided in a cubicle house in Nova Scotia, used 10 kg sand/cow/day in the cubicle bed plus 5 kg sawdust/cow/day in the passage. The cows were very clean and lameness was at a low level.

Outbreaks of lameness are often seen when cows which have been previously housed in straw yards are transferred into a new cubicle building. The cows find the cubicles strange and less comfortable, lying times decrease, trauma to the hoof is increased and lameness results.

One of the worst outbreaks of lameness (sole ulcer and white line disease) I have experienced was associated with just such a situation. The straw-housed cows were transferred into a new cubicle house, the floors of which had been laid so that the front half was flat and the rear had a steep slope, producing a ridge in the centre of the lying area (Illus. 6.12) and very little bedding was used. The cubicles were obviously uncomfortable and very few cows used them properly. Many were standing, while others were lying half in the cubicle and half in the dunging passage, or totally lying in the dunging passage.

The beds were re-laid with an even 100 mm fall from front to rear, and additional bedding was provided. Cubicle usage increased and eventually the lameness subsided. Those cows which had severe ulcers never fully recovered and many had to be culled.

Cubicle Design

Overall cubicle size and the design of the divisions both have an effect on cow comfort. Cubicles should be at least 1.2 m wide and 2.2 m long *(32)*. If possible, allow another 1–1.2 m at the front for a lungeing space, that is an area into which a cow can move her head when getting up. Illus. 6.13 shows the movements a cow makes when standing and the need for the forward space.

Length is probably the most important dimension

6.13   A cow may lunge forward for a distance of 1-2 m when rising naturally.

and seems to have the greatest effect on cow acceptance, although many cows are happy to lunge to the side if the cubicle design allows this movement. The Dutch cantilever shown in Illus. 6.14 would provide sufficient space, although Illus. 6.10 shows an even better design with more lungeing space. Compare this with the cow in Illus. 6.15 – she will find it very difficult to rise. When the cow is lungeing forward her head stays very close to ground, so there should be the minimum obstruction at this level.

Many cubicle designs other than those in Illus. 6.14 are available, and those such as the cantilever type in Illus. 6.10 are currently very popular. The side rail of the cubicle is often as high as 1.2 m to give maximum room.

The cubicle should also provide sufficient forward space for the cow to extend her neck when regurgitating the cud (59). If a cow is forced to sit with her head to one side and with pressure on her rumen from the side divisions of an undersized cubicle, she may need to stand, front

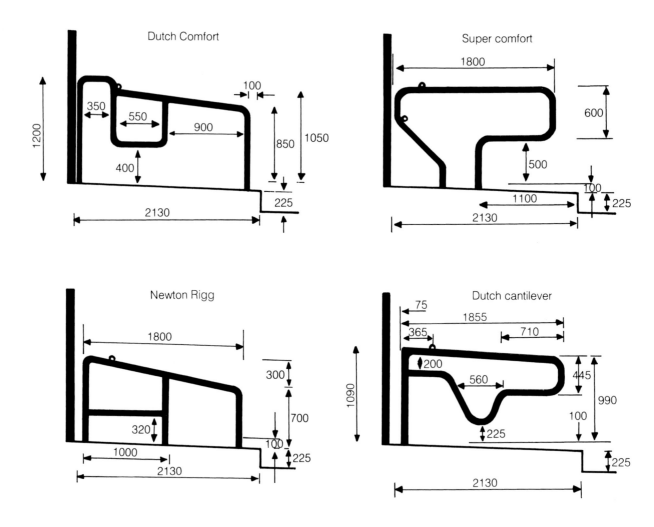

6.14   A range of cubicle designs with figures given in mm. *(Dr J. O'Connell, Moorepark)*

6.15   This cow will find it very difficult to lunge and stand.

feet in the cubicle and hind feet in the dunging passage, in order to ruminate properly. Excessive standing and corrosive slurry can both lead to foot problems.

Cows like a clear space at the front of the cubicle, and not a wall or some other rail. If the cubicle faces onto the feed passage, then it is best to remove the dividing wall. It does not seem to be important that the cows can move through from one side to the other across a double row of cubicles. Very few cows do so, and even if they do it is better than getting trapped when they try to stand.

Traditionally it was considered that excessively high cubicle steps were bad, because cows do not like reversing out of a cubicle and stepping down. However, a large UK survey *(6)* showed that there was more lameness in herds with a lower (15 mm) cubicle step. This could of course be because it is modern dairy units which usually have a lower step, but they also have higher yields and therefore more lameness. Whilst steps 200 mm or more high might lead to cubicle rejection, excessively low steps can encourage cows to lie with their tails

in the gutter, leading to soiling and more mastitis. The most important aspect of step height is cubicle training. If heifers have been trained to use high steps well before they enter the milking herd, then it will not be a problem.

Width requirements are to a certain extent affected by cubicle design, in that narrow cubicles can be partly offset by divisions which allow space sharing. For example, it is best to minimise the size of the cubicle division. The old Newton Rigg cubicle (Illus. 6.16) had the disadvantage of two

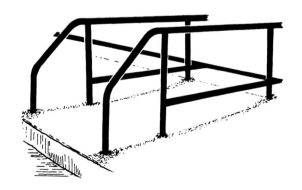

6.16   Newton Rigg cubicles bedded with straw.

vertical bars at the rear which can cause damage to the cow's pelvis, and a lower horizontal bar at the front that reduces side lungeing space.

The Dutch Comfort type shown in Illus. 6.14 has more space at the rear of the cubicle, but there is still an upright that could lead to trauma, and there is insufficient side space at the front to allow side lunging. Some heifers may get trapped in the small loop at the front if they move too far forward in the cubicle.

Full cantilever cubicles (Illus. 6.14) are ideal because they have no rear upright and there is good side lungeing space at the front. The bottom edge of the rear loop should be no more than 560 mm above the bed level, however, otherwise smaller cows will lie sideways on and soil the beds. In older buildings a length of rope under tension can be used in place of the lower cubicle rail (Illus. 6.17). The square edges of the wooden uprights in the cubicles in Illus. 6.18 could lead to injury.

6.18 Excessively narrow home-made cubicles. The cows found these uncomfortable.

In Illus. 6.19 the cubicle beds had been recently concreted, thus decreasing the distance between floor and rail. Cows damaged their hocks, leading to hock swellings (Illus. 6.9), abscesses, general discomfort and a further reluctance to use the cubicles. If cubicle divisions are too low, cows may try to pass underneath and get trapped. This is what happened to the cow in Illus. 6.20 which subsequently developed a haematoma (blood blister) on her back. Cubicle division heights of 1.4 m and above are currently being used and appear to improve cow comfort.

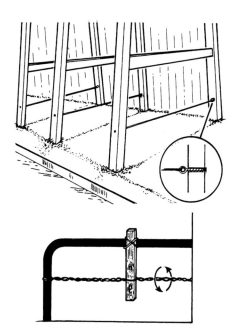

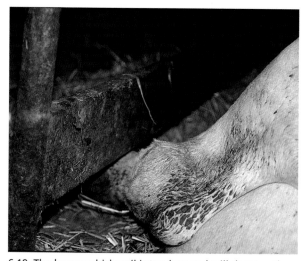

6.17 The lower cubicle can be replaced by a rope under tension. In the lower diagram a two-stranded rope is brought under tension by rotating a piece of wood (see arrows) fixed between the two strands. When the rope is taut, the wood is tied to the top cubicle rail.

6.19 The lower cubicle rail is too low and will damage the cows' hocks.

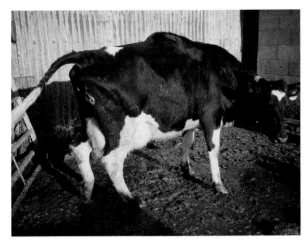

6.20 Haematoma on a cow's back caused by poor cubicle design.

The position of the front neck rail is critical. Too far forward and the cow can still dung on the cubicle bed when she stands up, thereby increasing the risk of mastitis. Too far back or too low and the rail makes the cubicle so uncomfortable that cows start to lie in the passageways, thus making lameness worse.

Although most neck rails are fixed to the top of the cubicle division, this is not necessarily the ideal position. This is of even greater concern if the top rail of the cubicle is too low (less than 1.1 m), as is the case on many traditional systems. A suspended rail, positioned 100-150 mm lower than the withers of a standing cow, as in Illus. 6.21, will increase cubicle

acceptance without producing excessive soiling of the beds. Brisket boards are also very useful if positioned correctly at 1.73 m from the curb, but make sure that they do not have sharp edges that could cause trauma to the knees when the cow is rising. Brisket boards position the cow correctly when she is lying, and neck rails position her when standing. Both are needed to keep cubicles clean.

Cubicle passages 3 metres or more wide (Illus. 6.22), reduce lameness (6) in two ways. First, a wider passage leads to less accumulation of slurry and hence reduced digital dermatitis. Second, a wider passage makes the building much less threatening for lower-ranking animals such as heifers, which are then more likely to enter to find a cubicle, thereby reducing lying times. In Illus. 6.22 the passage is especially good because there is also a large amount of bedding present. This producer, from a cereal-growing area, was using 4.5 kg of straw per cubicle per day, and this provided excellent comfort.

Some of the narrowest cubicles I have ever seen were home-made, using heavy timbers, and fitted into an existing building. The cubicles were of varying sizes, with some as narrow as 910 mm (Illus. 6.18). The head of a bolt used to attach the lower rail protruded into the restricted space and was worn smooth from the cows continually knocking against it. The owner admitted that the cows did not like using these cubicles!

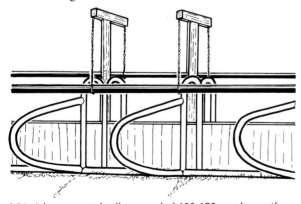

6.21 A heavy metal rail suspended 100-150 mm lower than the withers height of a standing cow is better than a conventional neck rail which is often fixed to the top of the cubicle division.

6.22 This is ideal for the cows. A wide passage with ample straw.

Modification of existing cubicle houses by constructing new cubicles in a herring bone arrangement (to increase cubicle length and width without changing the curb or passageway) have not been successful because the cow does not then lie square in the cubicle.

In one trial *(77)* where preference for cubicle design was assessed by recording the length of time that each cubicle was used, Dutch Comfort and improved Dutch Comfort cubicles were found to be superior to basic Newton Rigg. The different designs are shown in Illus. 6.14. However, in this trial, once a cow had accepted a particular cubicle type, the length of time spent lying was the same, irrespective of cubicle design.

Heifer Training

Without doubt, one of the most important facets of cubicle comfort, acceptance and lying times is heifer training. After the stress of calving, they have enough to cope with - learning a new system of feeding, entering the milking parlour and establishing their position in the pecking order - without finding that there is nowhere comfortable to lie down! If heifers cannot be reared in cubicles, house them for four to six weeks in the summer, whilst the cows are still at grazing.

An alternative is to mix heifers with the main herd, or even just the dry cows, for three to four weeks before calving. It may be a nuisance if non-lactating heifers enter a herring-bone milking parlour, but having to deal with lame heifers on a regular basis is likely to be equally as time-consuming, and if heifers have learnt to walk through the parlour prior to calving they are less likely to stand at the back and be last to be milked after calving. This will help to decrease standing times and hence slurry exposure in the critical post-calving period. If mixed with the dry cows, the heifers can be walked through the parlour twice a week, have a barrier dip applied for mastitis control, then back out through the foot bath to start the routine dermatitis control measures.

Building Design and Cow Behaviour

In addition to cubicle comfort, there must be enough space for cows to move around. Both feed and cubicle passages need to be wide (4.5 m and 3 m respectively), as this increases cow flow, reduces intimidation and also reduces exposure to slurry because wider passages effectively mean reduced stocking density. Ample loafing areas are ideal, especially if cows can move outside the building, although this increases potential slurry problems.

Conversely, overcrowding and inadequate loafing areas could mean insufficient exercise and consequently poor blood flow within the feet, especially during cold weather. A similar syndrome (known as 'trench foot') affected soldiers standing for long periods in muddy trenches during the First World War.

For low-ranking cows, cubicles can act as both a lying area and a safety zone, in that the side bars increase their effective personal space *(84)*. There is general agreement that there should be sufficient cubicles to allow all cows to lie down at the same time, with at least equal numbers of cows and cubicles *(93)*. Most people prefer to see 10 per cent more cubicles than cows, sometimes referred to as a 90 per cent occupancy. This means that an individual animal does not have to spend so long looking for a space to lie down.

Systems should also be designed with 'escape routes'. If cubicle passages are dark and blind-ended, heifers will be reluctant to enter because of the fear of being trapped by older cows, and hence lying times may decrease. Ideally there should be escape routes approximately every twelve cubicles. A narrow gap, just wide enough to allow a heifer to pass from one cubicle passageway to the next, is a help, although a double-width gap so that one animal can pass in each direction, is better. If, as often happens, the water trough has been sited in the cross-passage, then the double width is essential.

Avoid sharp turns. An animal normally turns a corner by walking slowly around it. If corners are sharp, or if heifers (especially) have to make sudden avoiding flight movements to escape from aggressor cows, turning will probably be achieved by pivoting on the sole of the foot. This has the effect of forcing the wall away from the sole, thus expanding the width of the white line and weakening it. Some older-style parlours have narrow exits where cows have to step down and turn sharply at the same time, often to walk back along the side of the same building, and this may increase lameness. Fixing a rubber mat onto the floor where they step down increases comfort, decreases friction, and in some cases has increased parlour flow rates because cows exit more rapidly.

A large number of cows jostling for position behind out-of-parlour feeders can have a similar effect, especially if slurry accumulates when they are queueing for food. Feeders are best spaced well away from each other, to reduce competition.

Keep the areas beside feed troughs clean and free from waste silage. Cows continually standing on waste silage may not wear their front feet sufficiently, and claw overgrowth may result, or if the area is soiled, it predisposes to digital dermatitis.

Collecting Yards

Cows spend a long time standing in collecting yards, so conditions need to be good. Yards need to be scraped after every milking, and pitted concrete, where slurry can accumulate, should be repaired. Yards should also be grooved, to ensure that they are not slippery. This reduces injuries from falling and also encourages cows to stand with their legs upright, i.e. not 'base wide' (legs apart), which is the position they adopt on a slippery surface. Collecting yards should be loaded

from the rear and there should be a straight flow from the yard into the parlour. If a yard is loaded from the front (Illus. 6.23[i]) the high-ranking cows (H) enter the yard first and move to the rear of the yard, and the low-ranking (L) and lame animals (L) enter last. When milking starts, however, the 'high' cows will push forward to the front of the yard to enter the parlour first (Illus. 6.23 [ii]), and as they do so they will push the lower-ranking and lame cows (L) to the rear of the yard. This produces an increase in agonistic movements at each milking.

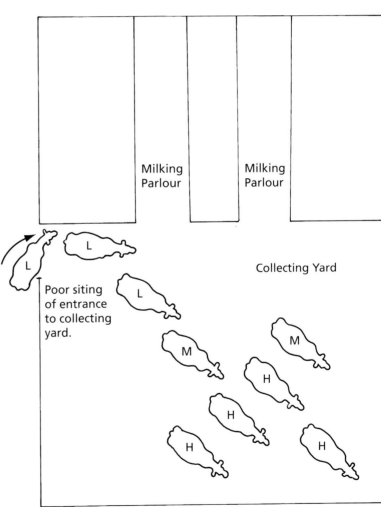

6.23 (i) Collecting yards should not be loaded from the front, otherwise high-ranking cows (H) enter first and pass to the rear of the yard.

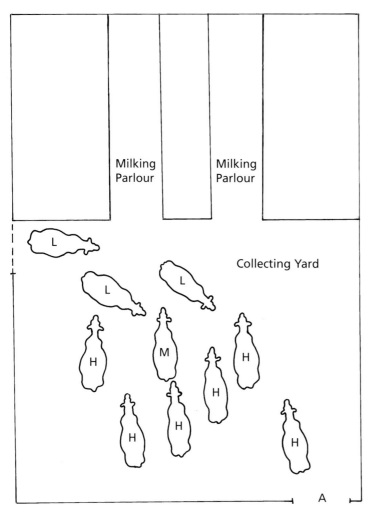

6.23 (ii) If the herd has been loaded from the front, high-ranking cows push past 'lows' leading to more agonistic movements.

Backing Gates *(Crowd Gates)*

The backing gate should be used to encourage cows to move towards the parlour. It should not be used to push cows forward, especially if it is electrified. A warning bell, telling the cows that the gate is about to move, is ideal. It has been shown *(29)* that cows congregate in small sub-groups in the collecting yard, and the sub-group will not enter until the lead cow has moved forward. If the lead cow stops for any reason, then the others will be reluctant to move past her. This is especially the case if they are tightly packed together because they would then have to make contact as they pushed past the lead cow to enter the parlour. A better cow flow will be obtained if there is more space around each cow. In theory, if the backing gate is used less aggressively, lower-ranking cows can pass their sub-group leader without the need for physical contact. If the crowd gate is used excessively, then cows will scrabble on their feet, and this can lead to lameness from hoof lesions. In addition, if cows turn suddenly or fall over they may well rupture the cruciate ligament in the stifle and then suffer an irreversible arthritis. Such lesions are not uncommon on dairy farms today.

A better system would be to load from the rear, i.e. at A in Illus. 6.23 [ii]. The high-ranking cows would then be at the front ready to enter the parlour first. Additional 'waiting lanes' at the entrance to the parlour where cows queue ready to enter are also of benefit. If the herdsman has to leave the rear of the parlour to encourage cows to enter, he needs to do so without 'facing' them and driving them towards the back of the yard. This system increases cow flow rates through the parlour, hence decreasing cow standing times, and improving overall time budgets.

Ideally, if the herdsman needs to go out into the collecting yard to move the cows forward, then he should be able to walk down the outside of the yard and then move them forward from the rear, rather than have to walk down through them and then turn them around again to face the parlour. This does not often happen. It has been suggested that there should be two sets of steps at the rear of the parlour, so that if you wish to get cows in from on the left side you exit from the right side, and vice versa.

Management Factors

Although the design of housing systems is important, the way in which cows are managed in those systems can also influence lameness.

Ventilation and Heat Stress

Cows are very wet animals, producing some 60 litres of water per cow per day in the urine, faeces, breath and sweat, the actual amount varying with temperature and humidity. It is therefore essential that buildings are well drained and well ventilated. Under UK conditions it is highly unlikely that cows will get too cold, and winter housing, especially, is as much to protect the land as to protect the cows.

On the other hand, high humidity levels in poorly ventilated buildings can lead to heat stress and decreased lying times with a subsequent increase in lameness. Heat stress is especially important in higher-yielding cows because they are producing more heat. One study *(36)* showed that cows started to react to heat at temperatures as low as 21°C, especially if the humidity was high. Lying times decreased by almost 30 per cent (from 10.9 to 7.9 hours per cow per day), and cows spent longer drinking (0.3 to 0.5 hours per day). They also cluster together in groups, rather than spread through the building, and they become much wetter, because they spend a considerable amount of time standing beside the water trough splashing out water with their tongues, increasing the overall levels of moisture in the building. With heat stress lame cows spend longer standing than non-lame; food intakes are reduced, and there is an increased risk of SARA, subacute rumen acidosis.

Collecting yards are especially important because the cows are crowded together for a longer period of time, and temperatures here are often 6°C higher than elsewhere in the building. This is yet another reason for a study of time budgets and reducing standing times. Buildings should therefore have as much air flow as possible. Remove external cladding for the summer, and remove as many internal walls as possible to improve air flow across the building. In the summer perspex sheeting in the roof is best covered to reduce the amount of radiant heat entering the building.

Wet Conditions and Slurry

Increased exposure to slurry increases the risk of lameness. This is because:

- Slurry is wet, and wet horn is softer than dry horn.

- Slurry increases the risk of digital dermatitis.

- Slurry erodes the heel horn, leading to a backward rotation of the foot, thereby increasing the risk of sole ulcers.

Wet conditions underfoot can lead to rapid softening of the hoof. This is common knowledge to us all: the best time to cut your toe nails is just after you have had a bath and not just before! Overcrowded conditions will both reduce lying times *(105)*, especially if cubicles are small and uncomfortable, and overcrowding will increase the level of slurry in the cubicle passages. Normal horn should contain about 15 per cent moisture, but this can almost double if the feet are continually in wet conditions. This weakens the hooves considerably - but makes them easier to trim!

Accumulated stale and corrosive slurry can increase the incidence of heel necrosis and digital dermatitis *(13)*, especially if cows are tightly housed in a poorly ventilated house with a high stocking density and low loafing areas. Cubicle passages should be scraped twice daily and stale areas of slurry avoided. The once- or twice-weekly sprinkling of slaked lime, used in cubicles for mastitis prevention, is probably also beneficial, in that it can harden and dry the hooves *(16)*. As discussed in the above section on comfort, a small amount of bedding pulled off the cubicle and into the passage (Illus. 6.11) acts as both a shock absorber and as drying agent for feet when the cow is standing half in and half out of the cubicle, a behaviour shown by a number of cows in any system.

Automated Scrapers and Flood Wash

One might think that automatic scrapers, leading to regular removal of slurry would be an advantage, but several authors *(6, 64)* have shown that there is a lower incidence of lameness in units with twice-daily tractor scraping. It is not known whether this is the effect of automatic scrapers pushing a wave of

6.24 Automated scrapers have been associated with increased lameness. This may be because of the wave of slurry, or because of removal of the small pad of bedding.

6.25 Flood wash systems have been associated with increased lameness, possibly because the cows' feet become wetter.

slurry along the passage, forcing a proportion of cows to stand in deep slurry (Illus. 6.24), or whether it is perhaps due to the removal of the small amount of absorbent bedding which is pulled from the cubicle into the passage. Perhaps it is simply because cubicle systems with scrapers often have narrower passageways. Flood wash cleaning systems (Illus. 6.25) have been associated with increased lameness, and especially dermatitis, possibly because the feet are wetter for longer, or perhaps because the recycled water used in some systems acts as a reservoir of DD infection.

Concrete and Rough Surfaces

Damaged and pitted concrete leads to pooling of water and can cause excessive bruising to the sole, producing small stones which can become impacted in the white line. Such concrete should therefore be repaired. When concrete is laid, a small round aggregate should be used and the mix kept dry. Wet mixes tend to wear more easily at the surface, thus exposing the aggregate. Flint aggregates should not be used. Their sharp edges are even more likely to traumatise the sole.

When cows first come onto slippery concrete they do the same as we do when we stand on ice - they move their legs apart in an attempt to maintain their balance. This means that the stride length is shortened and they therefore take more steps to cover a fixed distance when walking. This increases the trauma to the foot and also increases the probability of over-growth of the lateral claw. Floor surfaces should therefore be constructed to give good grip but without leading to excessive hoof wear.

Rough Handling

When cows move naturally, they walk with their heads down, watching where their front foot is to be placed, and the hind foot then follows in roughly the same spot. They also move in small groups of four to six cows, with the lead cow at the front *(28)*. When the lead cow stops, the remaining cows in the sub-group also stop, and the lead cow flicks her head from side to side, warning the other cows not to pass. The old, sick, lame and infirmed are usually at the rear of the herd.

It is therefore of limited value to behave aggressively in forcing cows at the back of the herd to move, because they have to wait until the high-ranking cows further forward move on. In an ideal world, the best way to improve cow flow rates is to provide a comfortable track which the cows enjoy walking along. Then they will proceed at speed.

It has been shown *(30)* that cows which are rushed along tracks, by pushing them with a tractor or using a dog, for instance, do not use or produce 'cow-favoured areas', and in these herds lameness is increased. Gentle handling so that the cow can avoid unsuitable surfaces and place her feet in her preferred position is therefore important. If the cows are being pushed ahead by an impatient stockman, it is the lame cows congregated at the rear of the herd which become tightly packed and are unable to use favoured tracks. Such behaviour obviously has important welfare implications, in addition to increasing lameness. If their heads are up, the cows are under too much pressure (Illus. 6.7 and 6.29).

Cow Tracks

Cows which have to walk long distances along flint gravel tracks will be particularly prone to white line disease and sole penetration. Both conditions have been shown to be more common in the summer *(88, 90)*. If given the option, cows will use specific tracks when walking in and out to pasture. We have all seen the foot marks and areas commonly favoured; often these are at the edge of the much harder tractor route (Illus. 6.26), which is in the centre of the roadway.

Specific walking surfaces for cows have been constructed alongside the concrete or

6.26 Favoured tracks are often at the side of a roadway. Cows prefer walking on a soft surface.

stone roadways used for tractors. One example is shown in Illus. 6.27 and 6.28. This system is quite expensive to install and maintain, especially in wet weather, and is now less popular. A trench 1 metre wide and 0.3 metre deep is lined with a type of geotextile membrane used in road construction. A drainage pipe is run along the base and the trench is then filled with stone aggregate, preferably with finer stone towards the surface. This is then covered with a second, reinforced geotextile membrane, with the edges of the membranes being covered by soil to hold them in position. Finally, a 50 to 100 mm layer of bark chippings or cundy wood peelings is placed on the surface.

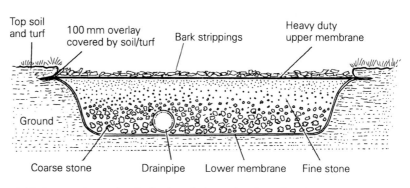

6.27 Cow tracks need to be both well drained and comfortable. They improve cow comfort, increase speed of walking and reduce lameness. *(John Hughes)*

allow cows to use the full width of the track. Where the stone track joins the inevitable concrete track leading up to the parlour, the concrete needs to be at least 100 mm higher to reduce the number of stones which are otherwise carried onto the concrete.

Concrete tracks should be regularly swept to keep them free of small stones – the effect of a cow with a soft sole standing on a stone on unyielding concrete can be dramatic. Make sure that tracks are not too steep – cows particularly dislike walking *down* steep slopes. If the track into the field is steep it can often be repositioned to run obliquely at a more gentle gradient. I have also seen tracks made from concrete railway sleepers, the junction between each sleeper providing grip on a gradient. Cow carpets are also available, sometimes using discarded carpets from marquees, and there is currently interest in the use of waste rubber products to form tracks. If possible, use separate tracks for cows and for tractors and farm vehicles, because the latter damage the surface.

6.28 A specially made cow track.

Although only one metre wide and thus allowing only single-file walking, the track is so comfortable that cows move quite quickly. Overall cow transit times are often less than if they were walking three to four abreast along a rough stone roadway. The reduction in trauma to the sole is bound to be beneficial, especially in the freshly calved animal.

Although these tracks were initially popular, they were found to have high maintenance costs. Compacted limestone or some other form of soft stone is now more commonly used. Cows do not like walking through water, so the track should have good drainage at the side and be built above ground level with a central camber to allow water to run off each side. Poor drainage and subsequent pooling of water is a common problem. It is essential to compact the stone with a vibrating roller. The base can be covered with a 25 mm layer of compacted quarry dust, possibly mixed with cement powder, to improve the final finish. Foliage on the hedges should be kept trimmed back to

Rubber Floors

Recent years have seen a big increase in interest in rubber flooring, although part of the evidence to support the benefits of rubber remains anecdotal. Illus. 6.29 shows how cows being taken back from milking along a concrete track prefer to walk on the narrow strip of rubber belting. Swedish studies have shown that, under conditions of low stocking density, cows will choose to walk on the rubber-covered section of the collecting yard and passageway *(10)*.

If rubber flooring is to be used, then it is most logical to fit it in the areas where cows spend longest standing, namely the feed passage (see earlier section on time budgets). Secondly, good use of it can be made in walkways to and from the parlour, or in the collecting yard itself. Illus. 6.30 shows a commercial farm system where the rubber has been fitted halfway across the passage for the past three years, so that cows are only standing on the rubber when they are feeding. The passage is

6.29 These cows are voluntarily walking on the rubber belting. Note that all the heads are down, a sign of comfort. *(K Burgi)*

tractor-scraped twice daily and the rubber does not appear to impede cleaning, nor has it become slippery. There has also not been a problem of cubicle rejection where cows have favoured lying on the rubber.

6.30 Use rubber where cows spend most time standing, e.g. at the feed face.

Using rubber flooring in the milking parlour, as in Illus. 6.31, is becoming increasingly popular. It is anecdotally reported to make cows more keen to enter the parlour (and hence speed up milking). Lame cows stand more quietly because they are more comfortable, and it is easier to detect mastitis when fore milking onto a black surface. Experimentally it has been shown that the horn produced by cows walking on rubber is of better quality than horn from cows on concrete *(101)* and that the cows' stride pattern is also more natural *(95)*, although field trials showing a decrease in lameness have been less conclusive.

6.31 Rubber floor surfaces in the milking parlour may make cows more keen to enter.

Excessive Exercise

Whilst excessive standing reduces blood flow in the hoof and is detrimental, excessive walking can lead to over-wearing of the soles. Soles that are less than 5 mm thick are soft and easily bruised. This soft sole syndrome is a common cause of lameness in heifers and in young bulls introduced into a cubicle-housed dairy herd. (See the sections on toe ulcers and soft soles in Chapter Five.) A heavy workload, resulting in excess wear on the hind feet, plus a reluctance to use cubicles (because of their size) often leads to lameness in bulls.

On lifting the foot, the sole is found to be worn so soft that it can be easily depressed with the thumb. In Illus. 5.42 note how the wall of the hoof has been worn away and that weight is now taken by the sole, leading to haemorrhage and sole fissures. Sometimes a white line infection is also present, especially at the toe, and this can lead to toe necrosis (Illus 5.43). Bulls working in cubicle-housed dairy herds should therefore be rested in a straw yard or loosebox, ideally for twelve hours on and twelve hours off.

If the soles of the feet of first-calved heifers can be depressed by thumb pressure, the animals should be housed in a straw yard for two to four weeks. Alternatively, an examination of the heifers' time budget may suggest some other way to reduce hoof wear. Failure to do this could result in the development of sole ulcers and sole penetration, in addition to the obvious welfare implications.

Excessively worn and soft soles can also be a problem in the large-herd grazing systems of Australia, New Zealand and South America. Heifers and dry cows may be held in a soft-surface calving paddock prior to calving, then on the day after calving, when the rate of horn growth is minimal, they are mixed with up to five hundred other cows, leading to increased social interactions and excess standing. They are then expected to walk 2 km along a hard stone track to the pasture and back, twice daily. Not surprisingly the hooves wear badly and soft soles, often with toe ulcers (Illus. 2.26) and white line lesions result. If, at the same time, the weather is wet, the hoof will be softer and wear will be even faster.

Inadequate Hoof Wear

It is also possible to under-wear hooves. The hooves of heifers reared and housed continuously on straw or in sand yards simply do not get adequate wear. This can lead to over-growth at the toe, a backward rotation of the hoof and pedal bone, pain, discomfort and a predisposition to sole ulcers, as described in Chapter Three (Illus. 3.9, 3.10 and 3.13). In addition, heifers reared on soft surfaces such as a straw yards have been shown to have thinner soles than heifers given some exposure to concrete before calving. The latter group is clearly more likely to be able to withstand the pressures of the early-lactation environment.

During pregnancy heifers should be given a strip of clean concrete against the feed face and water trough, sufficient in width to accommodate all four feet when standing eating or drinking. This will allow normal wear of the hooves; light trauma to the sole will stimulate sole horn growth, and the heifers will have learned how to stand on concrete. If over-grown front feet are seen, a sprinkling of sand on the concrete produces even better wear.

Similar considerations apply to milking cows, of course. If waste silage is continually present when they are standing at the feed face, this could lead to over-grown front feet. Keeping the area clean and applying a sprinkling of sand once a week could help keep the hooves in better shape. I think this would appeal to all of us who have had to trim front feet!

Dry Cows and Concrete Integration

Cows could be taken off concrete and, ideally, put out onto pasture for a while during the dry period (74), although this may lead to problems with feeding. Movement through grass helps to keep the hooves clean and heel horn then has an opportunity to regrow, thus alleviating the effects of heel necrosis and slurry heel. The cow has ample opportunity to lie down, but at the same time she has ample opportunity to take the additional exercise needed to compensate for her period of lactation confinement. Not only does this improve foot condition, but it also gives an opportunity for the traumatic injuries to knees, hocks and pelvis, shown in Illus. 6.9 and 6.32, to recover.

If the cubicles are uncomfortable, they may not be ideal for large, heavily-pregnant cows. However, one large UK survey of fifty dairy herds over three years showed less lameness in cows housed in cubicles in the dry period than in cows that were housed in straw yards and then moved to cubicles after calving (6). Possible reasons for this include:

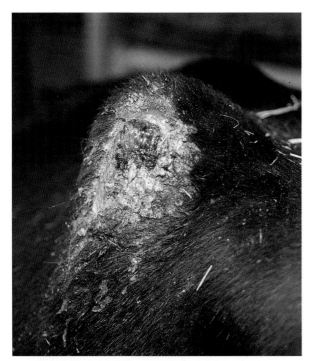

6.32 Discharge from a fractured wing of the pelvis originally caused by cubicle damage.

- Exposure to concrete produces a thicker sole before calving, which is then able to withstand the extra trauma and wear after calving.

- Heifers, especially, must learn to walk on slippery concrete. They stand with their feet further apart ('base wide'), and walk with shorter steps.

- Animals exposed to concrete and cubicles before calving are more likely to find a lying space after calving.

- Heifers mixed with the milking herd before calving will have undergone 'social integration' and will also be more likely to enter the parlour early on. Their collecting yard standing times will then be reduced.

Conversely, however, the same study showed more lameness in heifers kept with the milking herd during pregnancy than in those mixed with the dry cows.

Toxins, Breeding, Foot-Bathing and Trimming

Endotoxins

Any acute toxic illness can lead to horn production being slowed down or even stopped temporarily, depending on the severity of the illness. This was discussed in detail in previous chapters (e.g. page 26), where it was shown that this leads to changes in the hoof wall varying from hardship lines (Illus. 5.40) to a complete horizontal fissure (Illus. 5.38). Examples of toxic illnesses include peracute mastitis, acute toxic metritis, photosensitisation and foot and mouth disease. However, apart from FMD, toxins are less likely to produce lameness on a herd basis. Bacterial endotoxins from feed are discussed in the section on 'nutritional factors' earlier in this chapter.

Breeding

Genetics play a part in the production of lameness, partly through temperament and partly through conformation. Nervous animals are more likely to undertake sudden flight movements, tearing the hoof wall from the sole and hence weakening the white line, and are less likely to spend sufficient time lying down. Very heavy breeds seem to be more susceptible to lameness as are those animals with straight hocks, sinking pasterns, fetlocks almost touching the ground, feet turned outwards, claw rotation and hooves with a shallow angle of the front wall. Heavy breeds often have an increased incidence of interdigital skin hyperplasia (see Illus. 5.56).

As inherited conformational characteristics of both feet and legs have been shown to have a significant influence on the incidence of lameness *(74)*, bulls should be chosen with care. Suggested hoof and claw measurements are given in Illus. 3.3. Leg conformation is less important than claw conformation in terms of heritability, as it is thought that many of the leg characteristics are the result of bad feet, rather than the cause. For example, cows which walk throwing their feet out to the side probably do so because they have overgrown claws. However, excessively straight or angled hocks may lead to lameness: an angle of 100–150 degrees seems to be ideal (74).

Foot baths

The use of foot baths was discussed in detail in the section on digital dermatitis in Chapter Five, and they are only mentioned again here for the sake of completeness, emphasising their extreme importance in the control of lameness. Many people (17, 74) now recommend the daily foot-bathing of housed cows as an excellent preventive measure for lameness.

Solutions of 5 per cent formalin, 5 per cent copper sulphate, 2.5 per cent zinc sulphate, a variety of organic acids, and hydrogen peroxide, quarternary ammonium and glutaraldehyde disinfectants have all been used in routine foot baths. Routine disinfectant foot-bathing is considered to be beneficial in several ways:

- It disinfects between the claws and thus helps to prevent infectious diseases such as foul and digital dermatitis.

- It reduces the incidence of interdigital growths (skin hyperplasia - see Chapter Five).

- It disinfects the heel, thus reducing heel necrosis and preventing the destabilisation of the foot which results from a sinking heel (Illus. 5.20).

- it cleans and disinfects the foot and therefore improves the rate of healing of exposed corium following treatments for sole ulcer and white line defects.

The activity of formalin (and most disinfectants) is influenced by temperature. A warm bath (15°C) is most effective (74). Foot-baths obviously soon get contaminated, and for most farms the solution is best replaced on a daily basis. One study (57a) showed that on average 320 cows could pass through a 4 per cent formalin foot bath before the formalin concentration was reduced by more than 50 per cent. In the same study the participating farmers were asked to make up the foot bath to 4 per cent. However, when the

strengths of the made-up solutions were measured they were found to vary between 1.0 and 9.0 per cent! It is therefore important to check the mixing instructions. Extreme excess of formalin can cause superficial burns on the skin above the hooves, as shown in Illus. 6.33 and this seems to be a greater risk in the summer, perhaps because the feet are cleaner. The burn is only superficial, however, and if the formalin concentration is returned to acceptable levels, healing is rapid.

Foot baths will be much more effective if cows enter with clean hooves and are able to walk out

6.33 Extreme excess of formalin can cause superficial skin burns. This is not common, however.

the other side onto clean (scraped) concrete. Often two baths are used (Illus. 6.34), separated by a length of raised concrete. The first bath contains water to wash off excess dirt and the raised concrete strip allows feet to drain slightly before entering the active ingredient. Double-width foot baths (Illus. 6.35) are of value in larger herds because they promote cow flow. If one cow is hesitant to enter, but another cow passes by her and goes through the bath, then it will encourage the reluctant cow to move through. The greater bath width also makes the bath less intimidating, and cows are unable to stand on the sides of the bath. Double-width baths will of course be more expensive because they use more chemical, but they will become less contaminated.

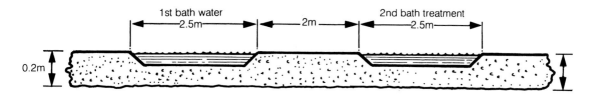

6.34 A dual foot-bath. The first removes dirt and debris and cleans the feet; the second contains the active ingredient.

6.35 A double-width foot-bath improves cow flow for larger herds.

Do not overfill the foot bath. The chemical solution only needs to be 60–70mm deep, just covering the hoof. Excessively deep baths are an unnecessary expense (in that they use too much chemical), the chemical may be too weak to be effective, or cows may be reluctant to enter deep water. There is also a greater risk of teat contamination from splashing.

Foot trimming

Perhaps it is appropriate to finish this book by listing foot trimming as an important measure in the control of lameness. Although regular trimming is generally accepted as beneficial, there are surprisingly few objective studies to confirm that this is the case.

One study used a weekly system of locomotion scoring (described in Chapter One) to assess the gait of cows. Cows with a score of 1 walked normally; animals with a score of 5 were acutely lame. It was found that cows which had trimmed feet walked better (i.e. had a lower locomotion score) and had a lower incidence of lameness than an equal group of cows with untrimmed feet in the same herd. The results are summarised on page 122 in Table 6.5 *(74)*. Cows with steeper claws (greater toe angle) and a shorter anterior hoof wall walked better and developed less lameness. There is, however, still considerable room for improvement. In a survey of almost two thousand feet in dairy herds in Somerset, UK *(32)*, 75 per cent of the feet were found to be overgrown or misshapen, with unequal claw size being the major factor. Over-trimming can be detrimental, however, especially if the soles are made too thin *(48)*.

Cattle hoof-care is therefore likely to be an important feature of dairy cow management in the future. Regular foot trimming will continue to feature prominently in the herdsman's daily routine, and I predict that regular, almost daily, foot-bathing will become commonplace.

	Trimmed	Not Trimmed	Probability of difference
Locomotion score†	1.52	1.83	* *
Number of lame cows	10	15	NS
Cases of clinical lameness	23	54	* * *
Weeks lame for clinical cases	2.30	3.43	* *
Solear problems	17	45	* * *

† Higher scores indicate more lameness

* * p<0.01; * * * p<0.001; NS p>0.05

Table 6.5. The effects of hoof trimming on lameness. Cows with trimmed feet walked better than those not trimmed. Fewer were lame and fewer suffered from solear problems (74).

A summary of Factors Causing Lameness

When investigating a lameness problem, consider the following factors.

Careful integration at calving

This is when the main stressors for lameness occur, and careful integration into the post-calving environment is required:

- *Environmental integration.* For example, heifer cubicle training. Some standing on concrete pre-calving both to acclimatise the heifers to hard surfaces and so that they learn how to walk on a slippery surface.
- *Social integration.* For example, mixing heifers with dry cows.
- *Nutritional integration.* For example, transition diets.
- *Other integration aids.* The following have been suggested as ways of helping to reduce the risk of bullying:
  - mixing heifers into the herd in groups
  - spraying them with cider vinegar
  - mixing at night.

Minimise standing times (and hence reduce hoof trauma) by:

- Correct integration at calving (as above).
- Optimising cubicle dimensions and comfort.
- Ensuring wide passages within buildings.
- Ensuring 10 per cent more cubicles than cows.
- Correcting cow flow to minimise cow standing times at milking (see time budget section).
- Adequate cross passages in cubicles to improve cow flow.

- Ensuring adequate feeding space to reduce standing times and minimise bullying This should be at least 0.6m per cow, and 0.8m for fresh calvers.
- Loading collecting yards from the rear and not the front, and ensuring good parlour flow.
- Reducing heat stress.

Provide good non-slip but trauma-free floor surfaces by:

- Giving attention to rough and broken concrete.
- Grooving concrete where surfaces are slippery.
- Ensuring cows are allowed to walk at their own pace.
- Construct proper cow tracks that allow comfortable, rapid and easy movement of the herd to and from pasture.
- Ensuring that cow flow does not involve turning sharp corners, especially if cows step down at the same time.
- Considering the use of rubber belting.

Optimise foot hygiene by:

- Ensuring cubicle and feed passages are of adequate width (e.g. 3 m and 4.5 m respectively).
- Regular scraping of passages.
- Avoiding automatic scrapers.
- Ample bedding, such that some falls into the passageway, thereby providing a softer, cleaner and drier walking area for cows.
- Avoiding the pooling of water and slurry by correct concrete levels, good drainage and attention to areas of pitting and pooling.
- Minimising cow standing times
- Regular, e.g., daily, foot-bathing.

Abbreviations

Anim. Prod. = Animal Production.

J. Dairy Sci. = Journal of Dairy Science.

J. Vet. Med. = Journal of Veterinary Medicine

Prev. Vet. Med. = Journal of Preventative Veterinary Medicine

Proc. BCVA = Proceedings of the British Cattle Veterinary Association.

Proc. 5th Int. Symp. = Proceedings of the 5th International Symposium on Diseases of the Ruminant Digit, Dublin (1986).

Proc. 6th Int. Symp. = Proceedings of the 6th International Symposium on Diseases of the Ruminant Digit, Liverpool (1990).

Proc. 7th Int. Symp. = Proceedings of the 7th International Symposium on Diseases of the Ruminant Digit, Denmark (1992).

Proc. 8th Int. Symp. = Proceedings of the 8th International Symposium on Diseases of the Ruminant Digit, Banff, Canada (1994).

Proc. 9th Int. Symp. = Proceedings of the 9th International Symposium on Diseases of the Ruminant Digit, Jerusalem (1996).

Proc. 10th Int. Symp. = Proceedings of the 10th International Symposium on Diseases of the Ruminant Digit, Lucerne (1998).

Proc. 11th Int. Symp. = Proceedings of the 11th International Symposium on Diseases of the Ruminant Digit, Parma (2000).

Proc. 12th Int. Symp. = Proceedings of the 12th International Symposium on Diseases of the Ruminant Digit, Orlando (2002).

Proc. 13th Int. Symp. = Proceedings of the 13th International Symposium on Diseases of the Ruminant Digit, Maribor (2004).

Proc. 14th Int. Symp. = Proceedings of the 14th International Symposium on Diseases of the Ruminant Digit, Uruguay (2006).

Vet. Rec. = Veterinary Record.

1   ADAS (1989), *Foot Lameness in Dairy Cows*, Publication No. 3206.

2   Amory, JR, Barker, ZE, Brassey, NR, Blowey, RW & Green, LE (2004), 'A postal survey of the incidence of lameness and claw lesions in dairy cattle in the UK', *Proc. 13th Int. Symp.*, pp. 197-9.

3   Amory, JR, Barker, ZE, Wright, JL, Mason, SA, Blowey, RW & Green, LE (2007), 'Associations between sole ulcer, white line disease and digital dermatitis and the milk yield of 1,824 dairy cows on 30 dairy farms in England and Wales', *Prev. Vet. Med., Nov 2007*.

4   Anderson, PH, *Proc. 6th Int. Symp.*, p. 59.

5   Arkins, S, 1981, *Irish Vet. Journal* **35**, p. 135.

6   Barker, ZE, Amory JA, Wright JL, Blowey, RW & Green, LE (2007), 'Management factors associated with impaired locomotion in dairy cows in England and Wales', *J. Dairy Sci,* **90**, *pp. 3270-7.*

7   Baumgartner, C & Distil, O, *Proc. 6th Int. Symp.*, p.199.

8   Bazeley, K & Pinsent, PJN (1984), *Vet. Rec.* **115**, pp. 619-22.

9   Bee, DS, *Proc. 5th Int. Symp.*

10 Bergsten, C & Mulling, ChKW, 'Some reflections on research in bovine laminitis', *Proc. 13th Int. Symp.*, pp. 53-60.

11 Blowey, RW (1999), *A Veterinary Book for Dairy Farmers 3rd Edition*, Old Pond Publishing, Ipswich.

12 Blowey, RW, *Proc. 6th Int. Symp.* p. 55.

13 Blowey, RW (1990), 'Digital dermatitis control', *Vet. Rec.* **126**, p. 120.

14 Blowey RW (1990), 'A simple treatment for heel abscesses and deeper foot infections in cattle', *Vet. Rec.* **127**, pp. 515–17.

15 Blowey, RW (1992), 'Diseases of the bovine digit', *In Practice* **2**, p. 85.

16 Blowey, RW (1992), 'Diseases of the bovine digit', *In Practice* **3**, p. 118.

17 Blowey, RW (2000), 'Control of digital dermatitis', *Vet. Rec.* **146**, p. 295.

18 Blowey, R W (2003), 'Can dairy cows become B vitamin deficient?', *Proc. TNVAC*, Florida, p.1107.

19 Blowey, RW & Sharp, MW (1988), 'Digital dermatitis in dairy cattle', *Vet. Rec.* **122**, pp. 505-8.

20 Blowey, RW & Williams, M, 'Use of a novel foam footbath in the control of digital dermatitis', *Proc. 13th Int. Symp.*, pp. 30-2.

21 Blowey, RW, Girdler, C & Thomas, C (1999), 'Persistence of foot blocks used in the treatment of lame cows', *Vet. Rec.* **14**, pp. 642-3.

22 Blowey, RW, Green, LS, Collis, VJ & Packington, AJ, 'The effect of season and age of lactation on lameness in 900 dairy cows', *Proc. 13th Int. Symp.* pp. 43-5.

23 Blowey, R W, Ossent, P, Watson, C L, Hedges, V J, Green, L E & Packington, AJ, 'Possible distinction between sole ulcers and heel ulcers as a cause of bovine lameness', *Vet. Rec.* **147**, pp. 110-12.

24 Blowey, RW, Sharp, MW & Done, SH (1992), 'Digital dermatitis', *Vet. Rec.* **131**, p. 39.

25 Boosman, R (1990), *J. Vet. Med.* **37**, p. 513.

26 Campbell, J, Greenhough, PR & Petrie, L, 'The effects of biotin on sandcracks in beef cattle', *Proc. 9th Int. Symp.*, p. 29.

27 Cermak, J, *Proc. 6th Int. Symp.*, p.85.

28 Chesterton, N, 'Linking farm physical conditions, herd management and cow behaviour to the distribution of lesions causing lameness', *Proc. 13th Int. Symp.*, pp. 200-2.

29 Chesterton, N, 'Lameness under grazing conditions', *Proc. 14th Int. Symp.*, pp. 138-40.

REFERENCES

30 Clarkson, DA & Ward, WR (1991), *Vet. Rec.,* **129**, pp. 511-12.

31 Colam-Ainsworth, P, Lunn, GA, Thomas, RC & Eddy, RG (1989), *Vet. Rec.,* **125**, pp. 573-5.

32 Collick, D, *Proc. 6ᵗʰ Int. Symp.,* p. 109.

33 Collick, DW, Ward, WR & Dobson, H (1989) *Vet. Rec.,* **125**, pp. 103-6.

34 Cook, N, 'Cattle practice', *Proc. BCVA,* Blackpool, 2004.

35 Cook NB & Nordlund KV 'Behaviour needs of the transition cow and considerations for special needs facility design', *Vet Clin North Am Food Anim Pract* **20**, pp. 495–520.

36 Cook, NB, Mentink, RL, Bennett, TB & Burgi, K (2006), 'The effects of heat stress and lameness on time budgets of lactating dairy cows', *J. Dairy Sci.,* **90**, p. 6643.

37 DaCosta Gomez, C, Al Masri, M, Steinberg, W & Abel, HJ (1998), Effect of varying hay/barley proportions on microbial biotin metabolism in the rumen stimulating fermentor RUSITEC', *Proc. Soc. Nutr. Physiol.* **7**, pp. 14-28.

38 David, GP, *Proc. 6ᵗʰ Int. Symp.,* p.1.

39 David, GP (1993), 'Severe foul-in-the-foot in dairy cattle', *Vet. Rec.* **132**, pp. 567-8.

40 Demirkan, I, Walker, RL, Murray, RD, Blowey RW & Carter, SD (1999), 'Serological evidence of spirochaetal infections associated with digital dermatitis in dairy cattle', *The Veterinary Journal,* **157**, pp. 69-77.

41 Demotec, Brentanostrasse 21, D6369, Nidderau 1, Germany.

42 Distl, O & Mair, A, *Proc. 6ᵗʰ Int. Symp.,* p.143.

43 Drew, B (1990), *Bovine Medicine,* edited by Andrews, Blowey, Boyd & Eddy, Blackwell Publications, Oxford, p. 45.

44 Eddy, RG & Scott, CP, *Vet. Rec.* **106**, p.140.

45 Esslemont, RJ, *Proc. 6ᵗʰ Int. Symp.,* pp. 37 & 276.

46 Garnsworthy, PC & Topps, JH (1982), *Anim. Prod.* **35**, pp. 113-19.

47 Giltspur UK (Cowslips), 13 Calhame Road, Ballyclare, Co Antrim BT39 9NA, UK.

48 Gonzalez Sagues, A, 'The biomechanics of weight bearing, its significance with lameness and the role of hoof trimming', *Proc. 14ᵗʰ Int. Symp.,* pp.18-23.

49 Green, LE, Hedges, VJ, Schukken, YH, Blowey RW & Packington, AJ, (2002) 'The impact of clinical lameness on the milk yield of dairy cows', *J. Dairy Sci.* **85**, pp. 2250-6.

50 Greenough, PR (1990), *In Practice* **12**, p. 169.

51 Greenough, PR, MacCullum, FJ & Weaver, AD (1981), *Lameness in Cattle,* Bristol Scientechnica.

52 Greenough, PR & Vermunt, JJ, 'An epidemiological approach to investigating bovine lameness', *Proc. 8ᵗʰ Int. Symp.,* pp. 186-94.

53 Hay, L, *Proc. 6ᵗʰ Int. Symp.*

54 Hedges, VJ, Blowey, RW, O'Callaghan, C, Packington, AJ & Green, LE (2001), 'a longitudinal field trial of the effect of Biotin on lameness in dairy cows', *J. Dairy Sci.* **84**, pp. 1969-74.

55 Hedlund, L & Rolls, J (1977), *J. Dairy Sci.* **50**, pp. 1807-12.

56 Hirst, WM, French, NP, Murray, RD & Ward, WR, 'The importance of first lactation lameness as a risk factor for subsequent lameness', *Proc. 11ᵗʰ Int. Symp.,* pp. 149-51.

57 Hoblet, KW, Weiss, W, Anderson, D & Moeschberger, M, 'The effect of biotin supplementation on hoof health', *Proc. 12ᵗʰ Int. Symp.,* pp.253-5.

57a Holzhauer, M et al., 'Measuring the concentration of foot-baths in dairy herds', *Proc. 13ᵗʰ Int. Symp.,* pp. 21-3.

58 Hughes, J, 'The cow and her cubicle', *Proc. 6ᵗʰ Int. Symp.,* p. 276.

59 Hughes, J (1992), *Proc. BCVA.,* p. 43.

60 Kameya, Y., Yamada, H, Abe, N & Matsuda, A, supplementary paper to *Proc. 6ᵗʰ Int. Symp.* published in *Proc. BCVA,* 1990-1, p. 7.

61 Kelly, JM (1990), data from *University of Edinburgh / Dalgety Spillers dairy herd health and productivity scheme,* 1987-90.

62 Kempson, S & Logue, DN (1993), 'Ultrastructural observations of hoof horn from dairy cows', *Vet. Rec.* **132**, pp. 499-502 & 524-7.

63 Kofler, J et al., 'Measurement of the temperature development on the corium using various grinding discs', *Proc. 13ᵗʰ Int. Symp.* pp. 106-8.

64 Laven, R (1996), 'The environment and digital dermatitis', *Cattle Practice* **7**, pp. 349-56.

65 Leonard, N, O'Connell, J & O'Farrell, K, *Proc. 7ᵗʰ Int. Symp.*

66 Lischer, CH & Ossent, P, 'Pathogenesis of sole lesions attributable to lameness in cattle', *Proc. 12ᵗʰ Int. Symp.,* pp. 82-9.

67 Livesey, CT (1984), *Vet. Rec.* **114**, p. 22.

68 Livesey, CT & Flemming, FL, (1984), *Vet. Rec.* **114**, p. 510.

69 Logue, DN, Bradley, H & Kempson, S, supplementary paper to *Proc. 6ᵗʰ Int. Symp.* published in *Proc. BCVA,* 1990-1, p. 38.

70 Maclean, CW (1965), *Vet. Rec.* **77**, p. 662.

71 Manson, FD & Leaver, JD, (1988), *Anim. Prod.* **47**, pp. 191-9.

72 Manson, FD & Leaver, JD, (1989), *Anim. Prod.* **49**, pp. 15-22.

73 Margerison, JK, Winkler, B & Stephens, G, 'The impact of clinical lameness on the milk yield of dairy cows', *Proc. 12ᵗʰ Int. Symp.,* p. 407.

74 McDaniel, BT & Wilk, JC, supplementary paper to *Proc. 6ᵗʰ Int. Symp.* published in *Proc. BCVA,* 1990-1, p. 66.

75 Mortellaro, C (1990), personal communication.

76 Nilsson, SA, *Acten Vet. Scand.,* **Vol 4**, supplement No. 1.

77 O'Connell, JM, Meany, MJ & Giller, PS (1991), *Irish Vet. J.* **44**, pp. 8-13.

78 Offer, JE, Logue, DN, Brocklehurst, S & Mason, C, 'The effect of an incident of the severe over-feeding of concentrates on claw horn lesion development in first-lactation dairy heifers', *Proc. 13ᵗʰ Int. Symp.,* pp. 175-8.

79 Ossent, P & Lischer, Ch, 'Sole ulcer: what's new about an old disease', *Proc. 11ᵗʰ Int. Symp.*, pp. 46-9.

80 Paulus, N & Nuss, K, 'Sole length, sole width, bulb height and sole surface area in cattle before and after functional trimming', *Proc. 13ᵗʰ Int. Symp.*, pp. 91-2.

81 Perusia, OR, 'Stay-on time of orthopaedic wooden blocks on cows in extensive feeding systems', *Proc. 14ᵗʰ Int. Symp.*, p. 144.

82 Peterse, DJ (1992), 'Foot lameness', *Bovine Medicine*, ed., Andrews, Blowey, Boyd & Eddy (Blackwell Scientific, Oxford), p. 353.

83 Peterse, DJ, Korver, S, Oldenbroek, JK & Talmon, FP (1984), *Vet. Rec.* **115**, p. 629.

84 Potter, MJ & Broom, DM, *Proc. 6ᵗʰ Int. Symp.*, p. 80.

85 Ral, R, *Proc. 6ᵗʰ Int. Symp.*, p. 219.

86 Read, DH, Walker, RE, Castro, AE, Sundberg, JP & Thermond, MC (1992), *Vet. Rec.* **130**, p. 60.

87 Repetto, JL & Cajarville, C, 'Nutrition and lameness; ruminal pH and sub-acute acidosis in grazing animals', *Proc. 14ᵗʰ Int. Symp.*, pp. 88-90.

88 Rowlands, GJ, Russell, AM & Williams, LA (1983), *Vet. Rec.* **113**, p. 441.

89 Rowlands, GJ, Russell, AM & Williams, LA (1985), *Vet. Rec.* **117**, pp. 576-80.

90 Russell, AM, Rowlands, GJ, Shaw, SR & Weaver, AD, (1982), *Vet. Rec.* **111**, pp. 155-65.

91 Singh, SS, Ward, WR, Lautenbach, K & Murray RD (1993), 'Behaviour of lame and normal dairy cows in cubicles and in a straw yard', *Vet. Rec.* **133**, pp. 204-8.

92 Sprecher, DJ, Hostetler, DE & Kaneene JB (1997), *Theriogenology*, pp. 1178-87.

93 Sumner, J (1989), 'Design and maintenance of housing systems', *Proc. Brit. Mastitis Conference*, Stoneleigh, p. 10.

94 Tarlton, J, et al. (2002), 'Biomechanical and histopathological changes in the support structures of bovine hooves around the time of first calving', *The Veterinary Journal*, **63**, pp. 196-204.

95 Telhezhenko, E, Bergsten, C & Magnusson, M 'Swedish holsteins' locomotion on five different solid floors', *Proc. 13ᵗʰ Int. Symp.*, pp. 164-5

96 Toussaint Raven, E (1985), *Cattle Footcare and Claw Trimming*, Farming Press Books, Ipswich.

97 van Amstel et al. (2006), 'The effect of parity, days in milk, season and walking surface on thin soles in dairy cattle', *Proc. 14ᵗʰ Int. Symp.*, pp. 142-3.

97a van Amstel, SR, Palin, FL & Shearer, JK (2002), 'Anatomical measurement of sole thickness in cattle following application of two different trimming techniques', *Bovine Practitioner*, **36**, pp. 136-40.

98 van der Tol, PPJ et al., 'The force and pressure distribution on the claws of cattle and the biomechanical effect of preventive trimming', *Proc. 13ᵗʰ Int. Symp.*, pp. 62-4.

99 Vermunt, JJ, 'Axial wall cracks', *Proc. 10ᵗʰ Int. Symp.*, p. 141.

100 Vermunt, JJ & Leach, DH, supplementary paper to *Proc. 6ᵗʰ Int. Symp.* published in *Proc. BCVA*, 1990-1, p. 4.

101 Voges, T, Benz, B, Lendner, G & Mulling, Ch., 'Morphometrical analysis of the microstructure of hoof horn and its interaction with flooring systems', *Proc. 13ᵗʰ Int. Symp.*, pp. 86-8.

102 Walker, RL, Read, DH, Loretz, KJ & Nordhausen, RW (1995), 'Spirochaetes isolated from dairy cattle with papillomatous digital dermatitis and interdigital dermatitis', *Vet. Microbiology* **47**, pp. 343-55.

103 Ward, WR (1992), *Proc. BCVA*, Wye, Kent, p. 120.

104 Whitaker, DM, Kelly, JM & Smith, EJ (1983), *Vet. Rec.* **113**, pp. 60-2.

105 Wierenga, HK & Hopster, H (1990), *Appl. Anim. Behav. Sci.* **26**, p.309.

Blowey, R.W. (1999) *A Veterinary Book for Dairy Farmers 3rd Edn,* Old Pond Publishing, Ipswich.

Blowey, R.W. & Edmondson, P. (1995), *Mastitis Control in Dairy Herds,* Chapter 8, Old Pond Publishing, Ipswich.

Blowey, R.W. & Weaver, A.D. (1991), *A Colour Atlas of Diseases and Disorders of Cattle,* Elsevier Publications, London.

Blowey RW (2004) *'Disorders of the Foot' in Bovine Medicine 2nd Edn,* edited by Andrews, AH, Blowey RW, Eddy R and Boyd H, Blackwell Scientific.

Greenough, P. R. (2007), *Bovine Laminitis and Lameness – a hands on approach,* Saunders Elsevier.

Greenough, P.R., MacCullum, F.J. & Weaver, A.D. (1981), *Lameness in Cattle,* Bristol Scientechnica.

Greenough, P.R. & Weaver, A.D. (1977), *Lameness in Cattle,* W. B. Saunders & Co.

Ossent, P. (1995), *'The Pathology of Digital Disease' in Cattle Practice,* vol. 3, p. 263. Phillips, C.J.C. (1993), Cattle Behaviour, Farming Press Books, Ipswich.

Tranter, W.P. (1992), *The Epidemiology and Control of Lameness in Pasture-fed Dairy Cattle,* a thesis presented to Massey University, New Zealand.

Weaver, A.D. (1986), *Bovine Surgery and Lameness,* Blackwell Scientific Publications, Oxford.

INDEX

Note: page numbers in *italics* refer to figures and tables

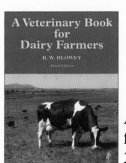
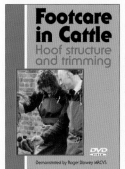

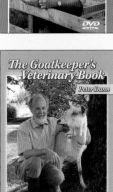